Ian Breakwell is an artist, video maker, television performer and diarist. Born in Derbyshire, he lives and writes in Smithfield, London. His paintings, drawings and prints hang in many public collections including the Tate gallery. His films and videotapes have been shown at festivals around the world.

Ian Breakwell's Diary 1964-1985

Pluto **Press**

London   Sydney   Dover New Hampshire

First published in 1986 by Pluto Press Limited,
The Works, 105a Torriano Avenue, London NW5 2RX
and Pluto Press Australia Limited, PO Box 199, Leichhardt,
New South Wales 2040, Australia. Also Pluto Press,
51 Washington Street, Dover, New Hampshire 03820 USA

7 6 5 4 3 2 1

90 89 88 87 86

Phototypeset by AKM Associates (UK) Ltd
Ajmal House, Hayes Road, Southall, London
Printed in Great Britain by Guernsey Press Co. Ltd.
Guernsey, C.I.

British Library Cataloguing in Publication Data
    Breakwell, Ian
    Ian Breakwell's Diary 1964–1985.
    I. Title
    823'.914[F]   PR6052.R3

ISBN 0 7453 0127 4

Acknowledgements

Some of these diary episodes first appeared in the following publications: 'Diary Extracts 1968–1976', Midland Group, Nottingham, 1977; 'Continuous Diary & Related Works', Scottish Arts Council/Third Eye, Glasgow, 1978; '5 × 5', Trigram Press, 1981; 'Witness', Transformaction, 1982; *Art Monthly*, Nos 56, 57, 58, 1982; '120 Days/Acting', Fernando Vijande, Madrid, 1983; *Aspects*, No. 23, 1983; 'The Waiting Room', Matts Gallery, London, 1985.

And in the television series 'Ian Breakwell's Continuous Diary' and 'Ian Breakwell's Xmas Diary', Annalogue Productions for Channel 4, 1984.

Introduction
by Nick Kimberley

Ian Breakwell has been keeping his diary for over 20 years. Pepys kept his for barely a decade, and abandoned it when the nightly activity of recording began to make him blind. Breakwell's diary, by contrast, opens up new possibilities of seeing – echoing, amplifying and extending his more familiar visual work. At times, the written and the visual are inseparable. At other times, they run alongside each other, or exist independently.

Breakwell actually began his diary, in 1964, as a purely visual account of his time. Inventing a day-by-day deadline for himself, he filled a four-foot-square panel with tiny drawings which, in a private way, reflected the day's minutiae. 'Nobody would recognize it as a diary,' he says, 'but that's what it was.' Soon, words were added. To begin with, the written diary was stripped of Breakwell's presence: 'I deliberately cut out all first-person references. Even if I appeared, it was usually in the third person. I was somebody else.' (Such dislocation of the self recalls Arthur Rimbaud's pre-psychoanalytic dictum, '*Je* est un autre' – '*I* is another'.) Little by little, the diary has assumed a more expansive form. The daily imperative has been abandoned, events now impose their own timetable. The short, highly condensed entries are balanced by the more discursive personal passages. 'I' is no longer so strictly avoided – although this selection closes, typically, with a babble of overheard pub conversation in which the only trace of the diarist is a hastily shouted 'Goodnight Ian' at closing time.

Ian Breakwell, as one of this country's most important artists, uses, perhaps more than any of his contemporaries, the whole scope of available media: painting, prints, photography and also film, video, tape-slide installation. The different segments of his work overlap, each enriching the other: and that includes the diary, which has been adapted for television.

It is rare for a contemporary artist to be given the opportunity of presenting work on television, and Breakwell has so far made full use of two chances to present a tele-visual diary. The idiosyncratic short segments, reflecting the different natures of each diary entry, defied conventional programming. The 'Continuous Diary' and 'Xmas Diary' used the medium to undercut televisual expectations. Extreme close-up would follow disembodied long-shot; spoken passages addressed directly to camera followed a scramble of distorted voices. Yet, despite the impact, the televised diaries seemed too specific to achieve the mysterious effects of the written version. Visualized and dramatized, events tended to take on a specific meaning which might be only one amongst the several in the written version – as if the condensed, understated prose allows the imagination a greater scope.

Nevertheless, the television series presented valuable opportunities to extend the diary's range, and its audience. For while it has always been accepted that Breakwell's writing must be seen as an integral part of his other artistic activities, the high visibility of his painting, film and video work has not been matched by a similar response to his writing, which has always relied on the circuit of small presses for publication. It is common for the most adventurous writing, in whatever form, to make its first impression outside the literary mainstream. This selection will allow a larger audience to read a key document of our time.

Thomas Mallon's survey of 'people and their diaries', *A*

Book of One's Own, divides diarists into chroniclers, travellers, pilgrims, creators, apologists, confessors and prisoners. Ian Breakwell is all of these – except apologist. As a chronicler, he gives us the trivial but intensely poignant details of modern living; as a traveller, his special province is the train journey. With a pilgrim's holy purpose, he reinvests the world with a sense of the miraculous and the impossible, and records the act of creation: of the diary, and of the films, videos, photographs and paintings which share a common genesis. The diary is also a confession of the myriad sins of furtive observation which are its essence. And Breakwell, like other diarists, is a prisoner, tied for ever to the compulsion to record.

The diary's landscape is primarily metropolitan. On the one hand, Breakwell revives Baudelaire's key imaginative figure of the *flâneur* who wanders the city streets, swept along by the crowds, taking his leisure in the pub, for ever listening and watching. On the other hand, the diarist is a solitary figure: perched high above Smithfield Market in his third-floor flat, he spies on the city, its people and its meat, aloof and sometimes cynical.

Elsewhere, he travels on the tube, breaking the Underground's first taboo: he stares. As he says, 'People do everything to avoid each other's gaze. They read newspapers on the tube because if everybody stared at the person opposite, it would become intolerable.' But Breakwell does stare, and lives to tell the tale.

For the diary, the city offers an alternative news bulletin to the one pumped out through 'official channels'. Headlines from the hoarding intercut with the huge blowups of advertising posters and overheard snatches of conversation: these are the hieroglyphics which give us our world picture. What we see on television only makes sense in chance juxtapositions: looking through a shop window at two TV sets, we see Auschwitz on one screen, a joint of pork in the oven on the other (3.2.1978). This is William Burroughs' naked lunch, forcing us for the first time to confront what we consume.

We don't like what we see. As John Lyle has said of Breakwell's writing,

'Not only does the Diary snapshot these absurdities and disjunctures, but it gradually allows the reasons for them to emerge: that because Reason is our method of control, our irrational behaviour frightens us and we learn not to notice it. To do so would lead us too close . . . to feelings of impotence, inadequacy, horror. We cease to see it, abetted by the media and all the forces which would preserve the status quo.

The diary can be seen as a latterday extension of the work of Mass Observation, that collection of artist-anthropologists who set out in the late 1930s to document a 'real' Britain by observing such 'mass' phenomena as 'Behaviour of people at war memorials, shouts and gestures of motorists, funerals and undertakers, the private lives of midwives', etc. Mass Observation was the brainchild of three men, Charles Madge, Tom Harrisson and Humphrey Jennings, whose origins were a long way from the masses of 'Worktown' which they set out to document. The project ran the risk of paternalism, but yielded vast quantities of fascinating material providing insights which, like a jigsaw, became a portrait of the time. Drawing comparison between Mass Observation, the British documentary cinema movement and surrealism, Angus Calder and Dorothy Sheridan assert that 'one aim was a kind of social therapy . . . a further aim might be social transformation.' Breakwell is a modern mass observer, though less distanced from the observed 'subjects'. He too sees a potential for both therapy and transformation in the smallest details. The very act of observing and recording reveals a significance all too easily glossed over.

Jeremy Lewison has pointed out, 'Breakwell is not an overtly political diarist and rarely records his reactions to major events.' Characteristically, one of the most 'public' events in the diary is the streaker who disrupted a test match at Lord's. The televized versions of the diary made much more explicit political statements. Here politics is approached tangentially, revealing itself in a phrase let slip, a chance encounter. Yet the purpose of the diary is wholly political, in the same way that the surrealists' project of permanent revolution took for granted that a transformation of the imagination would equally change society. The diary simultaneously demystifies the human condition, and reinvests it with mystery: there is a reality parallel to the one we know.

The parallel realities are exemplified in the recurring diary experience of train travel: here Breakwell finds himself almost literally between two worlds – the one outside the railway carriage, the other inside. Paul Hammond has said, 'What thrills [Breakwell] is the epiphany of momentary alignment and juxtaposition.' So it is that a fart let loose in the dining car of the London to Plymouth train can poleaxe a horse grazing by the side of the railway track.

For all the grime, for all that this life is no more lastingly substantial than the hunks of meat carted about Smithfield Market, for all that suppressed violence threatens to erupt from almost every page, the diary finds life constantly marvellous. The monstrous and the tragic exist cheek by jowl with the erotic and the laughable. Breakwell's epiphanies are every bit as enhancing as Joyce's – and less religious. Here, the marvellous is supremely human.

Quotes from Ian Breakwell are from an unpublished interview, January 1986. Other works cited: Angus Calder and Dorothy Sheridan, (eds), *Speak for Yourself: A Mass Observation Anthology 1937–1949*, Jonathan Cape, 1984; Paul

Hammond, 'Love Among the Pork Scratching', review of Ian Breakwell's 'Witness: More Diary Extracts 1976–1982' in *Art and Artists*, February 1983; Jeremy Lewison, 'Ian Breakwell: Caught in the Act', introductory essay to Madrid catalogue, 'Ian Breakwell: 120 Days / Acting', 1983; John Lyle, promotional leaflet for Transformaction edition of 'Witness', 1982; Thomas Mallon, *A Book of One's Own: People and their Diaries*, Picador, 1984.

Ian
Breakwell's
Diary
1964 – 1985

26.12.1964   Long Eaton, Derbyshire

The front room of the terrace house faces onto the street. The curtains do not quite meet in the middle. The walls of the room are white-embossed. On the wall is a brass-framed mirror; on the corner of the mirror a stuffed canary is perched. The ceiling is white-embossed, the carpet green with a yellow floral pattern. Grey, nylon-covered chairs; black, yellow and green nylon-fur cushions. On the wall a pair of brass bellows on which is a side view of a galleon hangs from a hook in the shape of a front view of a galleon. On the mantelpiece is a hat-shaped clock, a bell-shaped musical box, a swan-shaped flowerpot, and two empty candlesticks. On the brown carved sideboard, brown carved table, white-painted window ledge and veneered cocktail cabinet are white vases filled with paper flowers. The woman who makes the paper flowers kneels on the black nylon rug in front of the convector fire. She is 50 years old, plump like a cushion. She is talking to a poodle. The woman dresses the poodle in a green woollen suit, boots and hat. The woman's husband, who is sitting in a chair by the fire, takes off his shoes and socks, and his wife takes a polaroid photograph of the dog licking her husband's feet.

6.6.1966 Wales

Across the bridge, in the house overlooking the river, the host and his wife are entertaining guests to ham sandwiches, cake and tea. The host, a sparsely built man in his late thirties, is sitting at a low coffee-table, talking to two other men, both thin and dark, one aged 30 and the other aged 23. The younger man has a large bony nose and a drooping moustache. The host's wife is in the kitchen; she puts down a plate onto the floor to be licked clean by a young fawn whippet. The host's young daughter walks through the kitchen into the living-room; two black and white mice sit on her shoulders sniffing feverishly. The host's eldest son sits at a table, and from a box he empties scores of green toy soldiers onto the table. The host's youngest son is sitting by the window, planting a Venus Fly Trap in a pot. On the window ledge sits a large cat, staring across the fields as a train moves slowly along the railway by the river. The wife of the thin man with the drooping moustache, a small woman with long hair, is sitting on the floor, leafing through a glossy magazine and biting at the skin around her fingernails. The wife of the other man is sitting on the sofa eating cake. She is very fat. Her tiny breasts seem like one more fold of flesh. Her white stockings just cover her knees. She wears a very short skirt and sits with her knees under her chin. The younger son turns and stares out of the window, confused at the sight of her corrugated thighs. The fat woman scratches the inside of her leg, on which there is a large yellow bruise. The daughter carries into the room a cardboard box full of toy figures and animals, and begins to make a farmyard on the rug, helped by the small woman with long hair. The thin young man with the moustache leans over and picks out a tiny red plastic chair from among the toys; unnoticed he places it on the coffee table, and on the chair he places a plastic gorilla. He continues talking to the other two men; suddenly they catch sight of the

14

gorilla on the chair and burst into loud laughter. The host searches in the cardboard box and takes out another plastic chair, and places on it, upside down, a hippopotamus which is three times as big as the chair; on the hippopotamus's upstretched legs he places a tennis ball. Soon a whole array of toys cover the table: a farmer with a pitchfork sticks a pig; another pig is being ridden by a huntsman; yet another has its head stuck in a skating boot; a pelican carries a baby's arm in its beak; a lion sits on the wings of a biplane. The three men continue to move the toys into new situations. The daughter and the long-haired woman continue to build their farmyard. The fat woman on the sofa throws back her head, snorting with laughter. The host's wife walks in from the kitchen and smiles at the toys on the table. The oldest son is feeding a fly to the Venus Fly Trap. The cat stares out of the window at a train moving along the railway.

17.7.1967   Bristol, 1 a.m.

The woman walks over the bridge by the station, wearing a bra, pants and stockings and clutching a black dress to the front of her body; as she passes the young married couple she pulls down her pants as far as her knees to reveal her white buttocks. In this condition she runs as best she can up the grass verge and stands pensively in the road. Tightening the bath towel around her head, she climbs into her car and follows the couple to their house, and when they enter their house she takes the car into a U-turn and drives away very fast across the crossroads.

1.2.1970

Because of engineering works the Swansea–Bristol train is detoured along the Severn Estuary. Midway along the estuary the railway follows the bend of the river, and the river here is about 400 metres wide. In the centre of the river is a sand spit just showing above the water; the sand spit is about 250 metres long, isolated in the centre of the river, water on every side. A man is running down the centre of the sand spit; he has reached halfway when the train enters a tunnel.

19.4.1970

Because of engineering works the London–Plymouth train is diverted along the Thames, and then via Swindon and Chippenham. Shortly before reaching Westbury the train passes a hollow in a field, separated from the houses behind by a natural bank of earth. In the hollow, about ten metres from the railway track, stands a man with his trousers and underpants round his ankles and his sweater rolled up under his armpits. He leans backwards, exposing himself completely. With one hand he massages his stomach and with the other he waves vigorously at the train. His mouth is wide open.

22.4.1970   Taunton–London train, 3 p.m.

The husband and wife sat with the dog between them. The dog was on a lead tied to the man's arm. They stroked the dog. The man stroked its head and the woman stroked its stomach. The man unwrapped a box of chocolates and candies. The man and his wife examined the different varieties. They fed each other with chocolates. The woman held a chocolate above the dog's nose. The dog snapped at the chocolate. The woman held the chocolate higher. The husband fed the wife another chocolate; she held it in her lips before eating it. The dog snapped continuously at the chocolate in her hand. She dropped the chocolate into the dog's mouth. The dog swallowed the chocolate whole. The dog licked the inside of the woman's hand. The man shook the chocolate box against the dog's ear. The dog bit the chocolate box. The man held the dog's head and the woman pulled the box out of the dog's mouth. Then they tried it with a cigarette. The dog bit at the cigarette; tried to eat it. The dog's saliva soaked the end of the cigarette. The woman put the cigarette in her mouth and lit it. The dog thrust its head inside the man's jacket, snuffling at the crotch of his trousers. The man lay back, laughing, gripping the dog by its neck. The woman held the dog's back legs.

16.7.1970

At a certain point on the motorway between Beauvais and Paris it was not possible to see the headlights of the van coming in the opposite direction. All that could be seen through the coach window was a glowing Michelin man, seated with crossed legs and moving slowly nearer through the darkness, one metre off the ground.

20.9.1970 London, on the banks of the Thames, an ivy-covered power station

Some people train ivy to grow all over the outside walls of their houses, so that they can pretend they are living in a tree.

I remember a night in spring 1964. It was 3 a.m. and I was on Cologne railway station with five hours to wait for a train. I was in a long corridor, the walls and ceiling lined with white tiles. I sat on the floor with my back against the wall. The corridor was completely empty. I was on the verge of sleep when from a small grill in the wall behind my head came an ear-splitting *Achtung!!!*

As a child I could never understand who owned the wall which separated our yard from the next-door neighour's. Was it ours or theirs? Eventually I decided that we must own halfway through each brick.

When I lived in the top-floor flat of an old Victorian house in Bristol the walls began gradually to move. When it reached the stage where I could see daylight between the wall and the window frame I mentioned the problem to the building repair man. He said there was no need to worry because the walls 'were moving outwards'.

I once met a man in a bar in Exeter who claimed to have torn up the walls and floor of a padded cell. That was the only interesting thing he said all night.

One summer I worked in a factory in Derbyshire. Across the road from the factory was a yard surrounded by a high wall topped with cement into which were set jagged pieces of broken glass. The yard contained nothing but a pile of rubble.

I saw a newspaper photograph of Israeli soldiers standing with their backs to the camera, kissing the 'liberated' Wailing Wall. It looked exactly like a line of men having a piss.

A winter's night in 1966. I am sitting in the Scala Cinema, Bristol, watching a film called, I think, *The Other World of Winston Churchill*. Generals Eisenhower and Montgomery are describing in tones of awe the artistic stature of the great man as the brick wall that Winston built at Chartwell fills the screen. On my left is an old woman cracking walnuts with her teeth; on my right is a man dressed in a raincoat, swimming trunks and sandals.

In Paris in 1969 a squad of government employees with rolls of stone-coloured wallpaper would each morning go round the walls of the district covering up the previous night's slogans.

When I was about 8 or 9 years old my cousin from Melton

Mowbray came to stay with us. What had happened was that she and my aunt were watching television in their cottage when it was struck by lightning. The whole of the facing wall was ripped away, leaving them sitting looking out into the field.

2.2.1971

The Plymouth–London train, somewhere between Westbury and Reading, in the countryside. On the left of the track is a high bank of earth covered with shrubs and undergrowth. Lying on his side in the undergrowth is a man in a black overcoat; his face is contorted as if in pain; he is shuffling a pack of playing cards.

4.5.1971   The train from Penzance to London

The train is passing through green countryside west of Reading. In the middle of a field: a young girl in a white, flounced dress; a big black and white dog; a white metal barricade. The girl pirouettes on her toes and the dog jumps over the barricade. The girl pirouettes and the dog jumps over the barricade. The girl pirouettes . . .

18.5.1971   The Plymouth–London train, north of Castle Cary, 6.50 p.m.

In a field surrounded on all four sides by a hedge is parked a Ford estate wagon. Standing with their backs to the car are two old men; they are casting fishing lines into the middle of the field.

21.5.1971

Crossed line

Woman: '... well I've put the washing out so it better stay fine.'
Man: 'I think it will.'
Woman: 'I think it will too, it said on the forecast it would.'
Man: 'Well, the sun's shining here.'
Woman: 'Is it?'
Man: 'Yes, been shining all morning.'
Woman: 'Typical isn't it?'
Man: 'Mmmm,'
Woman: 'Yes.'
Man: 'Mmmm,'
Woman: 'Well, I must ring off now, I'm going to have my hair done.'
Man: 'Ah well, never mind, I'll piss all over it when I get home.'

6.6.1971   The London–Plymouth train, somewhere between Pewsey and Westbury.

A grass-covered hillside; a ploughed patch on the hillside; in the middle of the ploughed patch, a boat.

19.6.1971   London: Finsbury Library

A tall sun-tanned man, aged about 30–35 years, is standing in front of a case of books (a variety of Bibles and biblical dictionaries). The man is wearing a blue jacket, off-white shirt and blue tie, grey flannel trousers wide at the top and tapering to narrow bottoms, very large black shoes without heels like a clown's. He works methodically along each bookshelf from left to right, picking out each book in turn. He lifts out each book in such a way that as he holds it in his hands the book is upside down. Standing upright he riffles the pages, breathes heavily, replaces the book and takes out the next one.

13.10.1971

The man is in the library again. He has a new method of looking through the books: he riffles through first from front to back the right way up, and then from back to front upside down. This time he is working through the Ancient History section; when I leave he has reached Early Sparta.

17.11.1972

Travelling in a taxi past London Zoo. Over the wall is a big cage, in the centre of which is a tree without leaves. Two men in boiler suits are crawling towards each other on their stomachs along the branches on either side of the tree.

1.1.1973   12.03 a.m.

Central Amsterdam is like the scene of an urban war, as deafening fire-crackers, rockets and flares go off continuously in every street. On one side of the street a poker-faced youth with long hair, dressed in a combat jacket, is launching rockets from a pipe halfway up a wall at the entrance to a dark alley. Expressionless, without any outward sign of emotion, he extends his hand behind and a small boy hands him another rocket. The youth launches a rocket about every ten seconds, and each rocket follows the same trajectory, narrowly missing the corner of the building opposite, two floors up. On the second floor of this building a man in a white shirt, blue tie and black trousers, stands on a balcony at an open window. A few feet back from the balcony, inside the tastefully furnished apartment stands a woman in a two-piece trouser suit, a Labrador dog by her side. Every ten seconds the woman hands the man on the balcony a firecracker which he throws, each time with the same jerky arm movement, across the street below, his face expressionless. The firecrackers explode close to the side of the dark alley from which the youth is doggedly launching his rockets. At 12.45 a.m. the youth in the alley and the man on the balcony simultaneously run out of ammunition. The man on the balcony closes the double windows and draws the curtains. The youth and his assistant disappear back down the alley.

7.1.1973   By rail from London to Somerset

Day train

The right eye, nearest the window, sees the changing landscape outside. Changes of space and distance: the train moves alongside high stone walls in which there are gaps which give a view across the sea. Changes of lighting: within one mile the train passes through open fields, a forest, a tunnel, then open fields again.

Occasionally, something outside the window catches the traveller's attention. A chance occurrence. These unrelated scenes form a random relationship in the mind's eye during a long journey: a church with a small graveyard in the middle of a ploughed field; a man looking through binoculars from the top of a grass-covered mound; a flock of sheep huddled together; the embankment burning, an old aeroplane circling overhead; two black swans against the sky; an obelisk on the edge of a small cliff overlooking the golf course; bales of straw roll across the field towards the canal, along which moves a horse-drawn barge; a rabbit runs across the white horse carved in the hillside; across a field runs a grey asphalt single-lane road which is terminated in the middle of the field by a stone wall.

The left eye sees the fragmented scene inside the train; the backs of heads, the backs of hats above the backs of seats; cigarette smoke drifts around the corner of the seat; eyes look over bags and clothing piled on the table tops; faces bisected by newspapers, front-page photographs, fragments of head-lines; food goes into mouths; faces are powdered; lips are lipsticked; mouths smile, grimace, laugh, yawn; fingers scratch, rub, adjust clothing; knees twitch under the table; feet tap.

Sometimes the train passes an embankment or a row of trees and the scene inside the train is reflected in the windows, superimposed on the landscape outside.

The sun sets. The figures of the passengers are silhouetted against the landscape. The inside and outside scenes are now permanently merged by reflection. Darkness falls.

Night train

Outside the landscape is black. Lights move through the darkness. Some buildings are illuminated. The reflections of the brightly lit interior now dominate. Distorted reflections of faces in the double-glazed windows; eyes blurred, two sets of lips. Across the gangway sits a woman in a pink-ribbed sweater. Her image is reflected in the window alongside her and in the window alongside me, which is in turn reflected in the window alongside the woman, and so on like a Chinese puzzle. Her permed head and uplifted torso moves steadily through the darkness across the landscape alongside the track: sails across a river, rushes through a tunnel, cruises along a motorway passing cars and trucks.

People pressed into the corners of their seats, the muscles tense in their faces; they shift uncomfortably as they try to sleep. Men slumped on table tops, sleeping with their heads resting on their arms, the reflections of their frowning faces moving through the fog outside the window. Two girls, half awake, touching the veins on the insides of each other's wrists with their tickets; sleep settles on them; one girl opens an eye and looks at the other girl who is slipping down in the seat; a faint smile; her eyes close.

The train moves through dimly lit stations. Past platforms stacked with mailbags. Past platform benches on which sit people hunched up against the cold; their faces flinch and twitch as the train rushes by. Past men standing beside the track, their legs brightly illuminated by the lamps lying on the ground, the rest of their bodies in darkness. Over the rooftops of the housing estate the reflections of four travellers chewing with their mouths shut. Tired sailors sit with tattooed hands over their faces; multicoloured designs: flying eagles, pirates waving cutlasses, Indian chiefs, dragons, snakes, battleships, coats of arms, mottoes, the Dance of the Seven Veils.

23.1.1973   Above Triscombe, on top of the Quantock Hills, Somerset, 10.30 a.m.

Heavy frost; temperature below freezing; clear sky and bright sun. A man on horseback comes down the path alongside the quarry. He is dressed in old but immaculately clean and pressed riding clothes. His face is raw and set hard. Through clenched teeth he says: 'Good morning.' Slight flicker of his eyes. Across the open ground from the hilltop other riders can be seen gathering. In the small clearing in the woods the bushes are white with frost. The silence is broken by the sound of horns and shouting from the far side of the woods.

The noise gets nearer and nearer. Up the track comes the fox, moving steadily about 100 metres ahead of the pack of yelping dogs. The fox is big and old; it cuts into the woods. The fox moves out of the wood a few metres away, then disappears into the trees on the far side of the clearing. The dogs are all around, snuffling in the undergrowth. The rider with the dogs calls to them in a singsong military voice. Other riders arrive: one in a red jacket; a youth dressed like a show-jumper; three old men in black jackets and black bowler hats, all with the same cold, hairless faces. Another pack of assorted dogs arrive and fan out across the clearing. Gradually the barking recedes into the distance. Looking from the hilltop, riders and dogs can be seen scattered over a wide area of open ground, moving slowly in different directions.

27.1.1973 Queen's Park Rangers Football Ground, Loftus Road, London W12

The man in the football crowd pulls a whole fried chicken from inside his overcoat, pulls off the legs and wings and passes them across the face of the man alongside him to his friends on the other side, leaving him with the body, which he grasps in both hands and eats during the first 15 minutes of the match. The first goal comes unexpectedly in the fifteenth minute, and he throws his arms up, the chicken carcass flies into the air, half-chewed flesh and skin shoot out of his mouth.

8.3.1973   London, the aftermath of the Old Bailey car-bomb explosion

A City financier is hailing a taxi; he is immaculately dressed in a dark-blue business suit, except that the left trouser leg finishes a few inches above his ankle; blood oozes out of the laceholes of his polished black shoe.

An old man with a bandaged head, his face the colour of ear wax, is walking along the street; he sinks to the pavement without a sound.

Two hours after the explosion office workers are still trying to make their way home from the City, a task made more difficult by the sudden rerouting of traffic, free-access parking and a national rail strike. Long queues of people wait at all the bus stops, and as usual they all look 'normal', patient and self-contained, except that looking closely you notice that the man in the grey overcoat is keeping his hands in his pockets to stop them shaking, but his lips give him away. Further down the queue an office girl whose hair is permed and blonde at the front is a redhead at the back, her hair dyed with blood. Her friend stands beside her, smoking a cigarette, the tiny pinpricks of blood on her stockings already congealed.

14.3.1973   London

At the traffic lights is an open-top Mercedes sports car with the engine running. A fashionably dressed young man sits behind the driving wheel, and by his side sits his fashionably dressed girlfriend, just like in the adverts. The traffic lights stay on red and the young man lights a king-size cigarette with one hand, smiles at the girl, and switches on the windscreen washers with the flick of a switch. Two jets of water arc into the air, over the top of the windscreen: one lands on his cigarette, and the other in his girlfriend's lap.

15.3.1973 Bermondsey Street, behind London Bridge Station.

A clear, sunny afternoon. Men are unloading packing cases by means of a crane from the second floor of a warehouse. A young man with shoulder-length styled hair, flared trousers and built-up shoes, walks out of the alley alongside the warehouse, carrying in his hands a live pigeon. He holds up the pigeon to show the men in the loading bay, and says: 'I'm going to fuck it.'

6.4.1973 London, a District Line tube train via Charing Cross.

A young woman, seated and dressed in a very expensive and conservatively cut tweed jacket, tweed skirt and kid-leather boots, her hands folded in her lap, looking straight in front of her, her face set like an advertisement for a perfect complexion. At her feet an Air France travelling bag and various boxes indicate that she has just returned from shopping for clothes in Paris. Next to her sits a middle-aged man in a grey raincoat and shiny old trousers, a leather briefcase on his lap. His left leg is pushed across and is just touching the hem of the woman's tweed skirt. The man is reading two worn and thumbed pages from an old copy of a newspaper. His eyes are closed, shut tight, as he holds the newspaper pages close to his face, his head rolling, his lips moving and stretching continuously, small beads of sweat breaking out on his forehead.

22.4.1973 London: the British Museum, opening time

Outside the Museum gates is a traffic jam of coaches, taxis and cars, all carrying Museum visitors; in the side streets can be heard the horns of other vehicles trying to reach the Museum. The entrance steps are packed with Easter tourists huddled together under umbrellas and babbling in a variety of tongues. An American is planning a route with his family: 'I guess we'll start with the Marbles and work up from there.' The doors open and two queues file through. Bags are checked by security guards. Inside people fan out in all directions, stopping in front of a glass case for half a minute before passing on to the next one. A guard gives directions for the exhibition of drawings: 'Turn left at the Mummies, left again, first right, right again, then straight ahead until you reach the pink wall and you're there.' An hour later the Museum is jammed with thousands of visitors, shoulder to shoulder, steam rising from their damp clothes.

24.4.73 London: Two Chairmen pub, off Trafalgar Square

As I walk out from the inside lavatory a massive Alsatian dog leaps out from the group of people around the bar, its teeth bared and snarling as it goes for my arm; I spin round to protect myself and it rips its teeth into my clothing before someone grabs it by the collar. It is the landlord's dog. The landlord says: 'You're lucky it didn't break your arm, it can break bones with a single snap and that's the truth. You see, it's trained to attack.'

A boy says: 'That's right, it's trained to attack, the dog isn't to know, it's trained to attack.'

The barmaid, her face set and mean, says: 'You should be ashamed of yourself, tormenting a poor dog, saying, "Come

28

on. Come on." I saw you with my own eyes, it's people like you who make me sick.'

25.4.1973   London

At the corner of Great Marlborough Street and Poland Street is a window filled with artificial heads displaying ladies' hats in timeless styles: hats like those worn by delegates to the national Women's Institutes Conference. Inside is a warehouse containing hundreds more of the artificial ladies' heads wearing hats, each head a variation on the same theme: alabaster face on a long neck, turned slightly to the left or right, eyebrows plucked, lipstick on the closed mouth. In the distance one of the heads turns and says: 'Yes, can I help you?' 'Possibly,' I reply, 'I'm trying to buy some hatpins.' The lady says: 'Oh but my dear, hatpins are a thing of the past.'

21.5.1973   The car park of the 'Swan Inn', Kingston St Mary, Somerset.

It is almost dark. In the front seat of a saloon car sits a woman, and by her side, in the driving seat, sits a big dog. A man comes out of the back entrance of the Inn, carrying a glass of beer; he gestures to the woman in the car to wind down the window, hands her the glass of beer, and she then winds up the window again. The man walks away. There is sudden, agitated movement inside the car; the dog is panting; the woman pitches forward, her head disappears below the dashboard, then she reappears, the smashed glass gripped in her hand, broken glass between her lips. The woman has the dog by the throat with both hands. The dog's tongue sticks out the corner of its mouth. The man is hammering on the window of the car.

9.6.1973   London: a pub in Smithfield Market

The two middle-aged women sit at a table in the corner alcove. Their faces and clothes are neat, trim, and almost identical. Their knees form a right angle to each other's knees as they sit half-turned towards each other, their hands folded on their laps, each smoking a cigarette of the same brand. The cigarette packets are on the table in front of them, each packet containing the same number of cigarettes. In front of each woman is a gin and tonic with a small slice of lemon. They look not quite at each other but just past each other's right ear. They each have a fixed smile on their faces as they sing inaudibly in time to the juke-box.

16.6.1973   The Sheffield to London train, between Leicester and Kettering

The temperature is in the eighties. No clouds. The sun directly overhead. The cricket pitch by the side of the railway track is freshly mown, and two sets of stumps are already in position. In the batting crease stands a black crow about one-third as high as the stumps. At the other end of the wicket another black crow stands in the batting crease alongside the stumps. A black crow stands behind the stumps. Two more black crows stand approximately in the slips, another in the gully, one at silly mid-on, one at mid-off, one at backward square leg, two in the covers, and a particularly large black crow walks up and down the mid-wicket boundary.

27.6.1973   Exmouth, South Devon

The Annual Dog Show is being held in the Church Hall. The hall is filled with dogs and their owners, either parading up and down the floor or sitting waiting their turn. On the stage at one end of the hall is a table covered with a Union Jack flag and assorted silver cups. In front of the stage a bulldog, unable to walk, sits on its rump slobbering and panting. At the other end of the hall are ladies serving home-made cakes and teas. Occasionally a dog pisses or shits on the floor and a large lady wearing a pince-nez shuffles out with a small shovel and a bucket. There is an atmosphere of jealousy and rivalry; glances are cast over shoulders, eyes flick up and down other competitors and their animals. A whippet trots around the judging arena, led by its owner, a big fat man in a lightweight summer suit, who jogs alongside in his polished boots. The Fancy Dress has only one entrant, a border collie dressed in tennis sweater and shorts, and gripping a tennis racket between its teeth; the dog is led by its owner, an unsmiling youth with a nervous tic; as he collects his inevitable prize the other dog-owners applaud and all the dogs bark in unison.

8.7.1973   The 6.30 p.m. train from London to Plymouth

In the dining car, the fat businessman farts loudly and unexpectedly, and simultaneously by the side of the railway track a racehorse falls down.

10.9.1973   London

As on so many recent days, people file in and out of railway stations, offices and department stores as the buildings are evacuated and searched for bombs. The bar on Marylebone Station is half filled with lunchtime drinkers who have just settled down again to the drinks they recently had to leave, when there is yet another loudspeaker announcement and they all tramp out of the station and stand in the road. The station is searched, then everyone goes back inside, the ticket offices reopen, the barman starts serving drinks, and down the middle of the station comes a group of running women precariously balancing eggs on spoons. The winner breaks the tape. Flashbulbs burst. Loud cheers.

19.9.1973   London

The woman in the blue trouser suit walks around the thickly carpeted Bond Street art gallery, inspecting the expensive prints on the walls. She ignores the small, long-haired dachshund which grips the bottom of her right trouser leg with its teeth. She drags the dog along the carpet as she moves from print to print.

28.9.1973   Stibbard, Norfolk

He is walking down the narrow country lane. To the left of him is a continuous hedge about two metres tall. He becomes aware that someone is walking in step with him on the other side of the hedge. Every few metres the sound of this unseen person's footsteps pause, land heavily, and then quickly catch up with his own. He realizes that the other person is periodically jumping up and down, attempting unsuccessfully to see over the top of the hedge. This continues until he reaches the main road.

Her hair covers his face. They lie with their arms around each other in the warm bed. Up through the floorboards comes the voice of the woman in the basement:

'You bloody bogger! Fucking shithouse! Don't you dare come down to my door again you bloody sod you bloody shithouse! You should have died in childbirth, it would have saved us all a lot of trouble! Bloody money and you get fucked in the eye! Fucked in the eye you get you bloody bogger! Your dirty bloody room for your dirty bloody game! Your dirty bloody knives and your dirty bloody forks! Yes, open the window to let out the smell! And neighbours saying have you heard anything have you seen anything? Bloody prostitute! Bloody filthy sod! Your bloody Muriel and your bloody Agnes and your bloody Arthur and all the rest of the boggers! Yes, your bloody Agnes and your bloody Arthur! Yes, your bloody mother while you go and get a couple of hours in! Standing on the corner like a common slut you bloody swine! Your bloody mother! Don't you bring your shit down here again you bloody swine! Your bloody mother! I'll say it is! And your bloody neighbours day and night reporting saying have you heard anything have you seen anything? I'll say I fucking have! Yes I heard you last night and the night before you fucking shithouse! In there in the arsehole like fucking animals! And for a bit of money! A bit of dirty money! You fucking rotten shithouse stinking filthy swine pig! Have fucking less! Well I think you should know about the bloody worker and the bloody neighbour! And they do this and they do that! Oh yes, there's not much they don't do! Bloody sods the bloody boggers! Did you get your money's worth? Yes my word fucked in the bloody arsehole, yes they do that dance! And tea and bloody chat all day long with nothing else to do! Your own fucking daughter fucked in the eye for a bit of custom! Should have

33

died in childbirth your bloody doctor!'

5.12.1973   London: Clerkenwell Road, EC1

In the parked car at the traffic lights the driver is picking his nose while looking in the driving mirror at the driver of the car behind, who is red-faced and shaking his fist. The first driver turns round and sticks his tongue out. The driver in the car behind shakes both fists and spits against the windscreen. The lights change.

14.12.1973   London

The newspaper seller shifts his weight from foot to foot, rubbing his hands and shouting: 'Crisis latest! Crisis latest! They're murdering all the Germans and strangling all the Italians!'

18.12.1973   London: Oxford Street

The shop windows are packed with food, clothes, furniture, liquor, chocolates and toys. Shoppers throng the street, shuffling along laden with Christmas gifts.

The elegantly dressed young man stands with his wife and child at the head of the bus queue. The man behind nudges him as he tries to get past in order to get on the bus. The young man turns round, clutching his Christmas tree in his arms, and shouts through the branches: 'Don't you push me or I'll pull your bloody face off!'

24.12.1973   The M1 motorway, Leicestershire

Cars move alongside each other on the three northbound lanes of the motorway, in and out of the patches of fog. Behind the closed windows drivers and passengers silently mouth the words of 'White Christmas' in time with their car radios.

7.2.1974   London: Victoria Street, 2.30 p.m.

A dry sunny afternoon. An elderly woman in a fur coat stands holding a woven leather leash in her ringed and braceleted hand. The other end of the leash is attached to the dog's neck by means of a collar into which small jewels are inset. It is a little grey pug-dog, bow-legged and hairless; its wrinkled face looks up at its mistress as it lifts its left rear leg and a stream of piss runs across the pavement. Pedestrians step aside. The woman beams and says to the little dog: 'Well done! Well done!'

11.2.1974   London: St John Street, EC1, 11.30 p.m.

On the opposite pavement of the otherwise empty street are two smartly dressed youths. One youth is jumping up and down and letting out a series of piercing whistles. His companion is stretched out on the wet pavement, rolling over and over, backwards and forwards, a cigarette between his lips, until he hits his head against a metal bin containing old bones; he sits up, rubbing his head ruefully. The other youth is now running briskly on the spot, bringing his knees up hard against his chest.

12.2.1974   London: Smithfield Market

A man strides out of the main entrance of the meat market, wearing a pair of pig's ears fastened to his head; he walks across to his parked car, whistling loudly.

24.2.1974   Leeds

A man in a new overcoat and an astrakhan hat, the weekend shopping in his arms, walking along the pavement barking loudly like a dog.

17.3.1974   7.25 p.m. Leeds–London train

The woman in the corner seat wears a green velvet coat trimmed with imitation fur, and knee-length maroon suede boots. She falls asleep, sinking into the corner of the seat. Her red velvet skirt slides up around her thighs; her mouth falls open and is reflected in the window, superimposed on the night landscape outside. The train runs parallel with a motorway: cars and lorries rush into her mouth, their headlights on full. She wakes up, coughing.

15.4.1974   London: St John Street, EC1

An old woman dressed in filthy clothes tied up with string, her arms and legs covered with sores and wrapped in polythene bags; she is polishing the outside walls of Barclays Bank with a Kleenex tissue.

10.8.1974   London: Exmouth Market

A little boy presses his face against the window of the pet shop; his nose, lips and stuck-out tongue are squashed against the window pane, on the other side of which, nose to nose through the glass, is a snarling dog.

20.8.1974   London: Lord's Cricket Ground

The third day of the match between Middlesex and Surrey is proceeding slowly. A small number of spectators are dotted around the stands, some dozing in the warm sunshine. Unexpectedly the batsman hits an effortless six: a flick of the wrists sends the ball sailing over the leg-side boundary. A spectator, high up in the stand, gets to his feet and waits, smiling, as the ball drops towards him. The ball lands on his fingertips and there is a sharp cracking sound as the fingers of his right hand are broken back like sticks. The smile freezes on his face. He stares dumbly at his hand and is eventually led away by the nearest other spectator.

10.9.1974   London: Theobalds Road

In the middle of the two lanes of traffic the bow-legged dwarf marches up and down directing cars, indicating that a delivery van should wait, haranguing the driver when, like all the other motorists, he ignores the dwarf's shrill commands. The dwarf stamps his little boot and writes furiously in his notebook pacing round and round the traffic bollard which is exactly as tall as he is. A big fat woman crosses at the traffic lights and towers over the dwarf, who is purple-faced with anger. The woman wags her finger at him and says: 'You must learn to control your temper, or else you'll do some damage.' The dwarf brushes her aside as he shrieks orders at an articulated lorry.

19.9.1974   London: West Smithfield

From out of the entrance to the hospital come a variety of out-patients: hobbling with sprained ankles, hopping with broken legs in plaster; shuffling coronary cases, amputees on crutches. Across the road two small children imitate each patient's different movements.

31.12.1974   London: Notting Hill Gate Underground Station, 11.59 p.m.

The train has been standing at the platform for nearly ten minutes with the doors open. The compartment is filled with tight-lipped women with handbags on their knees, clutching theatre programmes. A London Transport official stands on the platform studying a stopwatch; at exactly midnight he signals to the driver who lets out an earsplitting blast on his steam whistle. The women in the compartment fiddle with their programmes, shuffle their feet and cough behind their gloved hands. At the far end of the compartment a Japanese youth gets to his feet, clears his throat, and says: 'Excuse me; Happy New Year.'

3.1.1975   London, in the pub

The Voice of Law And Order:
   'Now look, we are all a seething mass, make no mistake about that. We are no different to that plant in that pot! We are no different to that potato in the ground! We are no different to the beetle you put your foot on! We are no different to that fly on the lampshade and that crocodile in the Nile! We are all created equal. The beetles and the ants are the same as us, but they weren't given a noise to make. We speak the language that's all. But some are more equal than others, and when it comes to the terrorist let's face it, you're up against the planks. Give him a tenner and he'll drop an atom bomb. He thinks: a tenner, I can have a night out on that. So I say, let the planks fight the planks. Planks of wood versus planks of wood. It's the same all over the world: where you've got ignorance and backwardness you've got trouble. But the population of the Isle of Man are a mixture of Irish and Scots and they are the most peaceful people in the world. Why? Because they've got the cat. And that Irish plank who's lying there in hospital with his hand blown off through carrying a bomb, well give the fucker a bomb in his other hand and say: "Here you are, cop hold of that!" '

11.1.1975   Norwich, 10.05 a.m.

On the top of a distant building is what looks a heron, turning and swaying from side to side. I remember a Saturday afternoon last autumn . . .
   The crowd were pouring out of Queen's Park Rangers football ground after the match, swarming along the pavements, heads down. On the top of a nearby block of flats stood a big sea eagle, looking down on the street. In the flat immediately underneath the eagle the family were watching

television, except for mother who was standing at the window watching the crowds below, her round placid face a few inches below the talons of the huge bird.

6.2.1975   Bristol–London train, near Bath, Somerset

By the side of the railway track is a white house which has a new antique door with an inset leaded window and polished coach lamps on either side. The husband is cleaning the car on the gravel drive leading from the five-barred gate. The wife is polishing the handle of the wishing well. A bull is looking at them over the garden wall and sticking out its big red tongue.

25.3.1975   London: Farringdon Road, EC1

A man with one leg considerably shorter than the other, lurching along whistling 'I Could Have Danced All Night'.

5.4.1975   London: National Film Theatre bar

An elegantly dressed man and an elegantly dressed woman are sitting opposite each other. She is dressed in a two-piece suit, the skirt just above her knees, and black calf-length boots. He is dressed in casual wear: grey sweater and slacks with knife-edge creases. His hair is parted on the right side of his head. He is telling her who, in his opinion, are the most important French film directors, pausing only to adjust the creases in his trousers. She listens, the little finger of her right hand cocked as she holds her coffee cup poised above its saucer. As he speaks he breaks the seal on the carton of cream for his coffee, inadvertently squeezes the carton, and squirts a little jet of cream up her skirt between her thighs.

20.5.1975   London: an Italian restaurant, Charterhouse Street, EC1

At the window table sit a businessman and his wife. He is commenting on the texture of the avocado pears they have just eaten; he pauses to sample the wine and gives a nod of approval. She is carefully separating the flesh from the bones of her trout meunière. Behind them, a coach pulls up outside the window. The coach is filled with mongol boys and girls on an outing; they wave and grin. One boy presses his blubbery lips against the coach window, licking the glass. The businessman leans across to his wife and asks: 'How's the trout?'

4.8.1975   Lord's Cricket Ground: second Test Match between England and Australia

The temperature: 85°F. Australia are set to make 484 runs in 500 minutes.

The middle-aged woman next to me has, during the course of the day, drunk a cup of coffee, a cup of tea, a cup of orange juice, a cup of milk, a cup of blackcurrant juice, and now a cup of lemonade; each time, after the first sip she laughs nervously and says: 'That's quite refreshing John.' John, her husband, glances each time in exasperation at her, his face purple and strained because he still wears his jacket, tie and shirt, cavalry twill trousers and brogues, in spite of the broiling heat.

'Why don't you take your jacket off John?'

'Because the last time I did you sat on it and creased it, that's why,' he whines through tight lips.

An over is completed, the players change ends, and leaping over the boundary fence comes a fat, naked man who runs into the middle of the pitch and hurdles both sets of stumps, before running into the arms of two waiting policemen who lead him away.

Thinking aloud I say: 'I wonder how they're going to eject him from the ground in that condition?'

'I don't know,' says the woman nervously, as she pours another cup of lemonade and says: 'Mmm, that's quite refreshing John. Why don't you take you jacket off?' John stares at her with an expression of apoplectic hatred, his fists clenched.

13.8.1975   Cornwall

At last, away from it all! After a six-hour train journey down from London, a long walk along the cliff tops, a climb down the cliff face and then over the slippery rocks, here I am on the last rock on the promontary, nothing but the calm, empty sea all around. I stretch out in the sun, then a black rubber-clad figure rises out of the water at my feet, grins from ear to ear, and says: 'Hello Ian!'

1.9.1975   London: Lonsdale Road, W11, 3 p.m.

A woman stands on the pavement, holding a saucepan filled with mincemeat. She scoops dollops of the meat out with a wooden spoon, and drops them one by one into a neat row of dollops in the gutter, until the sauce pan is empty, then she wipes her hands and walks away. A car cruises round the street corner, pulls into the kerb, and reverses on to the heaps of mincemeat, squashing them flat.

19.9.1975   London: a public lavatory, Theobalds Road

In the lavatory bowl: a used piece of sandpaper.

24.9.1975   London: Ladbroke Grove, W11, 2.30 p.m.

A funeral hearse moves slowly along the street, bearing a flower-covered coffin. A black limousine follows the hearse. In the back seat of the limousine sits a woman with a veil over her face, polishing her fingernails.

2.10.1975   London: Smithfield Market, 10 a.m.

A man in a green jacket steps out of the entrance of the post office, into the path of a hurrying man who instantly freezes, his face turning purple, his lips curled back from his bared teeth, his knuckles white as he clenches them into fists, then a man walking behind and not looking where he is going, cannons into him, bursting the two polythene bags full of blood which he is carrying, as his face turns purple and he clenches his fists. The man in the green jacket nods and goes on his way, past the two men standing in a pool of blood.

28.11.1975   London: The Strand, 11.45 p.m.

A man cursing his reflection in a shop window.

30.11.1975   London: National Film Theatre bar

An aristocratic woman enters the bar; she wears a fur stole and carries a sequinned evening bag. Her face lights up with a

43

delighted smile as she gazes at an abandoned plate of half-eaten sandwiches on a nearby table. She stuffs the sandwiches into her evening bag and continues on her way, her eyes sparkling.

7.12.1975   London: St Paul's Cathedral

Behind the high altar: a man in a raincoat, crouched down and growling, his lips flecked with foam.

9.12.1975   Wimbledon: a fish and chip restaurant

The old women behind the counter are talking:
'What I'd like is a nice young man to take me home.'
'Well, how about him, second in the queue?'
'Who, him, you mean Jesus Christ? No, Jesus was always too pure for me even if I did go to Sunday school.'
'Well, how about a nice old man then?'
'There's some funny old men round my turning.'
'Ooh, nice!'
'Well, not for me. That's why I've advertised in the *Gazette* for an octopus.'

12.1.1976   London

I went into my local pub in Smithfield Market just before 10 p.m. There was the usual Monday night crowd, lorry drivers from Scotland and Ireland delivering to the meat market, and night workers from the nearby newspaper distribution depots. I took a seat at the bar, next to Ethel, who runs a boarding house for lorry drivers.

After a while I became aware of a girl, possibly in her early twenties, rushing agitatedly from one group of drinkers to another. She was thin, wild-eyed, her hair cropped short, her movements jerky and unco-ordinated. She wore black slacks, blouse, and a blue nylon overall. Her face was raw and strained, no make-up. The palms of her hands were ingrained with dirt. She blurted out semi-incoherent words in a loud rough voice. She was very disturbed.

I ordered another drink, and when I turned round again the girl had gone and so had the fat lorry driver at the corner table who had been buying her drinks. Obviously he thought he was onto a good thing.

'Where's that driver taken that girl, Ethel?'

'To his lorry. He's not fussy.'

A few minutes later the girl rushes back in; the driver comes back in the other door, shaking his head.

'She's mental, that one.'

'Call the cops, Joe.'

'I don't want any trouble.'

'She came in out of the blue.'

'She's run away from a home.'

'She's putting me off my beer, get her out.'

I begin to talk to her, persuade her to sit down and carry on talking. She begins to talk back.

'Audrey Wilkinson.'

'From a hostel. I ran away from a hostel.'

'Had a row with me mam this morning. I was in this boy's flat. She don't care. I am not going back to the hostel I'll tell you that. They treat you like muck.'

'They give me tablets but I don't take them.'

'I had a job before, scrubbing stairs.'

'Me sister Janet, she's in Plumstead but she's in court on Monday, she keeps breaking windows.'

'Our Janet's had treatment. They've give her treatment, electric.'

'You won't call the police, I've had enough of them, I'm

terrified of them, you won't call them.'

'I tell you what, I'd rather go home with you.'

'Him there, he's had too much to drink. He wanted to take me in his lorry where I didn't want to go.'

'I've got no coat, I'm freezing.'

Now it's closing time and I walk with her to the end of the bar to collect Ethel, who two drinks ago had said she'd come with us to St Barts Hospital round the corner, after Audrey had agreed to go.

'Right then Ethel, are you ready?'

'No Ian, I'm not coming. I've been told to keep my nose out of things. I'm not coming, no, I don't want to get involved.'

Audrey visibly stiffens. Luckily, Fred, a local caretaker is just leaving the bar and agrees to walk round to the hospital with Audrey and I, which we do. I explain the situation to the friendly night receptionist, and a nurse takes Audrey's arm and leads her behind a screen, and that's the last I see of her. I go home.

On Wednesday I telephone the hospital. The receptionist tells me that Audrey was admitted to the observation ward, but discharged herself during the night. They had no idea where she was now.

29.1.1976 London: Moorfields Eye Hospital, Annie Zunz Ward

The line of women in dressing gowns and black glasses hiding bandaged eyes sit in their armchairs staring at the colour television. On screen two American cops in black glasses stare back at them.

5.2.1976 London: The 'Casa Bella' Restaurant, Warren Street

A young businessman in a grey suit raises his knife above his head in a clenched fist; he breathes noisily through his flared nostrils, his teeth clenched. Gradually his breathing returns to normal and he continues eating his pizza.

6.2.1976 London: a pub in Smithfield Market

All the regulars are crowded together in the far corner of the bar near the fruit machine, shuffling their feet awkwardly and drinking with strained nonchalance. At the other end of the bar sits a lone drinker, staring straight ahead, and declaiming loudly: 'Germany's finished! Kaput! And under the bridge you never helped me. On Euston Station you said nothing. Well it's my war now. I'm baring my money. When you smell gas open your legs. I'm baring my money.'

With some difficulty the landlord persuades him to leave, and the regulars visibly relax, laughing and joking. After a few minutes the street door opens, the man's grinning face peers round the edge; a hush falls over the bar, and he says through clenched teeth: 'Is it safe to come out?'

7.2.1976 London: Queen's Park Rangers Football Ground

QPR are awarded a penalty despite the vigorous protests of the Wolverhampton Wanderers players. As the QPR captain prepares to take the kick, a blind Wolverhampton supporter in front of me covers his eyes with his hands: he cannot bear to look.

8.2.1976   London: St Bartholomew's Hospital, Paget
Ward (for female road traffic accidents). Early Sunday
morning

1st elderly patient: 'Are you having Communion?'
2nd elderly patient: 'No, I'm having a boiled egg.'

10.2.1976   London: St Bartholomew's Hospital

Patient: 'Phil's not too well, I hear.'
Visitor: 'No, he's died.'

12.2.1976

An institution in England

: the endless unlocking and locking of doors
: corridors
: steel doors
: pairs of shoes outside some of the doors
: observation holes in doors of rooms; just big enough to get a
hand through the one without armour-plated glass
: I wink at the eye in the observation hole; it winks back.
: I look through the observation hole of the next room: a girl
wearing only a short sweater is sitting cross-legged on the
rubber mattress in the bare room; she smiles back.
: Room walls scarred by fingernails
: room doors indented and battered by feet
: room floors, walls and beds stained by old piss and shit, like
a drawing endlessly erased.
: old and new fashions in straitjackets: some women
in traditional canvas jackets with thong back-lacing; one
in a prototype nylon floral design straitjacket, designed

48

and made in the hospital:
: a view through one window consisting entirely of rows of
keys
: the fourteenth door will not open: the problem is that
someone is simultaneously trying to lock the door on the
other side of the keyhole.
: a fully dressed woman in a locked side-room, lying on a
mattress in a pool of piss.
: a girl crouching on the floor in the middle of a locked room,
a handbag beside her, who has moved three feet to the left of
the position she was crouching in one week ago.

The day room

: behind armour-plated glass; furniture and fittings screwed
to the floor
: big inflatable bouncing balls with faces and ears on, to play
with
: a woman in a floral nylon straitjacket walking round and
round on tip-toes
: a woman banging her head continuously against the wall
: a girl in a canvas straitjacket with one arm free
: the nurse in tight blue skirt and black stockings kicks one of
the big inflatable balls with face and ears on, it hits the girl in
the canvas straitjacket behind the right ear, bounces off, and
wobbles to a standstill; the woman in the nylon floral
straitjacket walks round the ball on tip-toes.

The pre-release ward

: prefabricated; chintz; veneer; carpets; warmth; pots of tea;
curtains; bedside cabinets; pop-star pin-ups; snapshots of the
family; teddy-bears; soft toys; outside view of the concrete
security wall with an inset line of bricks about ten feet up as

decoration; Musak; just one girl asleep under the covers in bed, 3.30 p.m.; a big, sleek ginger tomcat lying on a bed; a set of drawings of skulls sellotaped on a bedside cabinet 'with love to Ethel'; gingham and pastel shades.

In the grounds

: swings with heavy iron chains
: a see-saw
: 'the pens': wire mesh cages surrounding scraped grass
: a pair of shoes with a name inside by a wooden bench

The recreation hall

: the stage with its massive pink proscenium arch. The same stage on which in 1955 I performed as a boy conjuror in a charity variety troupe, changing water into wine, cutting ropes and making them whole again, manipulating billiard balls, fanning cards, in front of the rows of faces staring dumbly from beyond the footlights and the uniformed nurses standing in the aisles. Some of the patients I have seen today would probably have seen my act 21 years ago.

18.3.1976   Long Eaton, Derbyshire, my home town: Leopold Street

My father worked as a machinist, a 'twisthand', in the lace mill on this street. Sometimes when I was a boy I used to take him his 'snap' at dinnertime: a flask of tea and sandwiches – beef, or beef dripping, or cucumber soaked in vinegar. The entrance to the factory was through a heavy wooden door and then up a winding spiral staircase, the stone steps worn down in the centre; the throb of the machinery two floors up gradually getting louder, then another heavy wooden door leading from the cool dark of the staircase into the heat of the machine shop; the smell of oil and the stunning noise, the oil-soaked floor vibrating, the rows of lace bobbins clattering up and down on their spindles, the teeth of the looms moving backwards and forwards. Then along the wooden walkways beside the machines until I came to where my father was standing in his blue overalls watching the bobbins and wiping the oil off his hands with a wad of cotton waste. You could hardly hear yourself speak. I had to put my mouth close to his ear and shout: 'I've brought your snap!'

He could not bear to watch oranges or tomatoes being eaten; if ever they appeared on the table he would leave the room. His chair was by the fire, facing the television set, alongside the standard lamp and the pair of brass bellows in the shape of a galleon. Hour after hour, night after night, he sat staring at the television, a one-pound bag of sugared almonds wedged between the cushion and the side of the chair. Every half an hour a Park Drive cigarette, the smoke sucked deep into the lungs, then blown out in a continuous stream across the room to swirl round the head of the highland piper on the top of the television set who turned round and round and played 'Scotland the Brave' when wound up. When I noticed that he was nipping his cigarettes out halfway down, I realized we were feeling the pinch. The dole and the pittance my mother was bringing in by making up nylon overalls on piece rate was not sufficient. The bottom had fallen out of the lace market. There were queues outside the labour exchange. Half time. One-third time. The odd day. Set on. Laid off. Each cigarette nipped out three times. A pocket full of nub ends. For one complete month he never uttered a single word to any of the family. My mother eventually broke down sobbing during a Sunday dinner, tears dripping into the gravy. My brother started bawling. I went and sat in the shed at the bottom of the garden.

The shed was full of bikes, spades, forks, tins of paint and varnish, brushes, hammers and saws. On the wall two photographs of my father looked down at me, one a football team photo, the other a studio portrait: pinned collar, tightly knotted tie, brilliantined hair, shiny new false teeth. On the shelf underneath the photographs were two of my grandfather's gallstones which he had given me as a present when he came out of hospital. As I stared at them they seemed like eggs laid by a stone bird. A thin, stooping bird with hunched shoulders and a grotesque hooked beak, crouching in a stone landscape, moonlit, at the foot of stone steps leading to a petrified forest. In the middle of the forest was a frozen waterfall. Bowler hats, umbrellas and briefcases lay beneath the waterfall, all turned to stone. Standing alongside the waterfall was a stone ladder at the foot of which lay a boy who had fallen, his arm twisted round his broken neck. The boy was calcified too: a fossil. Above the boy stood his father, a statue with pathetic outstretched arms which had tried to catch the falling child. In the town in the valley below the rocks the neighbours also stood like statues. Mrs Wilson, one foot on the step, about to enter the coalhouse. Mr Brown mowing the lawn. Mrs Cresswell leaning on her front gate, her hand cupped to her mouth, her forehead furrowed. In the field behind the street little Tony Cresswell turned to stone while running, around his waist a bag of exploding fireworks, his mouth open in a soundless scream, his eyes bulging. In the middle of the side street a group of children with pennies in their hands stood in a circle around backward Oscar, waiting for him to put the lump of dog shit in his mouth, waiting for ever because he, like them, was turned to stone, as was the small boy with his hands thrust through the bars of the playground gate as his mother finally turned to walk away and leave him to his first day at school. Both pavements of the town's main street were lined with children in uniforms, their arms half raised, their mouths half opened. The Queen sat in a stone limousine, her right hand raised, a smile fixed on her face like that of a ventriloquist's dummy.

Rain began to fall on the roof of the shed. The sky grew dark outside the window. At the corner of the windowpane a spider sat in the middle of its web. A fly landed on the web and the spider caught it, hurried back to the centre of the web and ate it.

The centre of the web. The eye of the needle. The winking eye in the plughole of the sink after the water has run out. The small, skinny boy standing in the washroom, pretending fascination as he stares down into the sink at the winking eye. Outside, the noise of his classmates racing round the playground. At the entrance to the washroom the school bully leans against the door, cracking his knuckles. 'Look,' says the little boy, desperately trying to buy time (eight more minutes to the end of playtime), 'look at the winking eye, isn't it fascinating?' 'Never mind that,' smirks the bully, 'come out into the playground.'

25.3.1976   A District line tube train between Edgware Road and Fulham Broadway

The spotty-faced youth sitting on the opposite side of the carriage is suffering badly from hiccups. He holds his breath until he is purple in the face, but to no avail. The hiccups wrack his slender frame, causing his adam's apple to bob up and down in his thin neck. He groans and leans forward in his seat, holding his head in his hands. The light bulb in the carriage ceiling above him drops out of its socket and crashes at his feet, narrowly missing the end of his nose. He sits up with a start, white-faced and wide-eyed. His hiccups are gone.

53

Men were playing bowls on the lawns in front of the vast redbrick building. The walls of the building were covered with ivy; the hundreds of windows were barred. The faces at the windows watched the bowls players and the men in ill-fitting suits who walked purposefully up and down the terrace in front of the bowling greens, their chins against their chests, their hands clenched behind their backs. Men in uniforms, their hands on their hips, watched the bowls players, the walkers and the line of men who had come out of the red-brick building and were assembling at the top of the terrace steps. In response to a signal from one of the uniformed guards the line of men moved down the terrace steps to a gate in a wrought-iron fence; the gate was unlocked and a guard counted them through and spoke into a walkie-talkie radio. The gate was relocked and the men moved down another set of steps to a green door in a red-brick wall; the door was unlocked and the men were counted through onto the cricket field, in the middle of which two sets of stumps were already in position. Some of the men sat down on benches around the boundary as the batsmen and fielders arrived at the wicket, others began to walk purposefully backwards and forwards. On the far side of the cricket pitch was a small pavilion alongside a big clock; behind the clock was a high red-brick wall. One man walked diagonally across the grass alongside the cricket pitch: it was a signal, and in the far distance on a hill, behind a wire fence and a high red-brick wall one of two figures raised her arm. The man stopped walking, smiled to himself and waved back.

18.9.1976   The Dome, Brighton

To the left of the proscenium arch: a man seated at a Wurlitzer organ, and a silver-haired man behind a drum kit.

The red velvet curtains part.

A woman in a skin-tight pink satin leotard, silver tights and pink stilleto-heel shoes stands in the centre of the stage. She is blindfolded; a round wooden stick is stuck in her mouth; on the stick she balances a solid rubber ball. From the Wurlitzer comes a sustained high note, building in volume as the woman opens her legs and executes a slow splits, the ball balanced precariously on the stick.

The curtains close.

The curtains open. On stage stands a young woman in a tight blue dress covered with sequins; her head is hidden inside the bell of a silver tuba.

The curtains close.

The curtains open. At the front of the stage stands a woman in a long white dress. Her arms are stretched out, her fists clenched. At the rear of the stage is a music stand supporting a glass disc on which is engraved a clock face with a black hour hand which is spinning. The hour hand comes to a halt at 11 o'clock and the woman quivers from head to toe as a tiny hammer hits the silver bell on top of the glass clock 11 times.

The curtains close.

21.12.1976   London: Blackfriars Bridge, 10.55 a.m.

A small group of people stand on the bridge, huddled together in the drizzle. Press photographers in hooded anoraks are checking their light meters. A police launch circles around on the swollen river. They are all waiting for the 'New Houdini', an escapologist who will at 11 a.m. be suspended over the River Thames from the bridge, upside down in a straitjacket from which he will escape.

11.30 a.m.

Everyone is frozen and wet. There is no sign of the escapologist, and people drift away muttering. On the other side of the road a man who is walking along the pavement steps on a steel coil which wraps round his ankles and trips him up; his head hits the pavement with a dull thud; he lies on the ground, his legs tightly bound together by the wire.

26.12.1976 London: District Line tube train between Edgware Road and Fulham Broadway

Two men in adjacent seats are engaged in intense discussion about the economic crisis, one man stressing the main points of his argument with emphatic gestures of his right hand, in which he grips his top set of false teeth.

7.3.1977 Manzi's Restaurant, Lisle Street, London

Brylcreemed waiters in white jackets glide purposefully between the tables carrying aloft large plates of salmon, trout, oysters, turbot, scallops, skate, smoked eels, crabs, Dover sole, halibut, prawns, lobsters, shrimps and mussels. The diners sit with their hands folded on the folded knapkins on their laps, watching intently as the food piles up in front of them until the whole table is covered with steaming fish. At the far end of the table a black man is playing the piano, tickling the ivories with podgy hands, a tortured expression on his face as he croons: '. . . a burnt-out cigarette with lipstick traces . . . an airline ticket to romantic places . . . these foolish things remind me of you . . .,' his brow furrowed, eyes rolling, lips drawn back to reveal sparkling white teeth set in bright-pink gums. The diners tip back their heads as they suck down their oysters. '. . . where little cable-cars climb halfway to the stars . . . and how are you sir? . . . enjoying yourself? . . . and how is your good wife? . . . and the children, I hope they are well? . . . good, good, that's fine . . . thank you sir . . . right on.'

11.3.1977   Smithfield Market, London

The traffic warden is laboriously writing a parking ticket, his tongue between his teeth, his brow furrowed. In the driving seat of the car a Labrador dog stares dumbly through the windscreen.

17.3.1977   London: an underground train ride from Waterloo to Mornington Crescent

Waterloo

The train is standing at the station platform. On the train, sitting side by side, are a young married couple. He wears a tweed jacket, a large tie, grey trousers and suede shoes; he holds a little umbrella on his lap; the fixed expression on his face seems to indicate constipation. His wife wears a knitted brown jumper, a grey skirt, and brown suede bootees lined with sheepskin; she grips a little umbrella; her face is bland and placid. On the other side of the train window alongside her husband's head are parted thighs in nylon stockings. On the other side of the train window between his head and his wife's is an armpit. On the other side of the train window alongside her head is a revolver. The doors of the train close and the train moves out of the station.

Embankment

The train pulls into the station. On the other side of the window alongside his head a Red Indian is about to fire an arrow from a bow. Between his head and her head is a stiletto-heeled shoe. She smiles blankly at him. He tightens his lips. Alongside her head is the face of a woman with her mouth open, her throat arched. The doors of the train close and the train moves out of the station.

Leicester Square

Alongside his head is a grinning man. Between his head and her head a hand is slipping inside the top of a pair of trousers. Alongside her head is the mouth of a shark. The train doors close and the train moves out of the station.

Tottenham Court Road

Alongside his head two children are walking hand in hand down a country lane. He fiddles with his umbrella. Between his head and her head there is a flash of lightning. She pulls at her cuffs. The train doors close and the train moves out of the station.

Goodge Street

Alongside his head an Indian guru is squatting in the lotus position. Between his head and her head a herd of cattle are moving slowly through the Grand Canyon. Alongside her is a man with eyes in the back of his head. She gives a little cough. The train doors close and the train moves out of the station.

Warren Street

Between his head and her head are a pair of buttocks in sheer nylon tights. He touches his lapels. Alongside her head is the face of a tiger. She strokes the little umbrella in her lap. He glances at her with a half smile which she returns. The train doors close and the train moves out of the station.

Euston

Between his head and her head a pair of breasts barely contained in a silk evening dress are thrust forward against the window. Alongside her head is a leather boot with a silver spur. They both give little coughs simultaneously. The train doors close and the train moves out of the station.

Mornington Crescent

Alongside his head a hand is stroking the bonnet of a limousine. Between his head and her head three people are seated in a train compartment: a young man and an elderly man with rolled umbrellas are casting sidelong glances at the knees of the woman who sits between them. Alongside her head is the face of a monkey with bared teeth. She smoothes her skirt and adjusts her knitted jumper. He straightens the creases in his trousers. They get off the train. The train doors close and the train moves out of the station.

25.6.1977   Herkules: Wilhemshöhe, Kassel, Germany

It was dusk. After the storm. Towering into the sky was the statue of Herkules, standing with one leg bent forward, hand on hip, leaning on a huge stone club. He stood on top of a stone pyramid which was on top of a massive building of rough-hewn stone blocks which housed a silent, empty pumping station. Thick mist muffled any sound except that of the water dripping from the archways and the high pine trees on either side of the ravine below. Black rooks circled overhead. A series of artificial cascades descended into the mist rising from the ravine. The hundreds of stone steps were covered with wet moss. The mist swirled and eddied. Grinning gargoyles loomed up for a moment and then were gone. Stone figures with puffed-out cheeks and bulging eyes leaned over pools full of fat golden fish lying motionless beneath the surface of the dark water. For a few moments the mist cleared from the ravine to reveal three men in overcoats seated on a bench far below, gazing into the mist in a second valley below them from which came the sound of distant trumpets.

26.8.1977 London: Smithfield Market, 9.30 a.m.

I was finishing my breakfast when there was a knock on the door. A black man was staring through the window. I opened the door. He stood silently and handed me a slip of paper on which were written the words: 'MISS JEAN.' I said I did not understand. His mouth opened wide but no sound came out. I realized he was dumb. Possibly deaf as well. He handed me the slip of paper again: 'MISS JEAN.' I handed it back. His eyes bulged and he began to make imploring gestures with his hands. I said: 'I don't think I can help you.' I wrote it down on the piece of paper: 'I DO NOT THINK I CAN HELP YOU. I DO NOT KNOW MISS JEAN. SORRY.' He went back down the stairs, a look of abject despair on his face.

Moorgate Underground Station, 10.15 a.m.

I am sitting on a bench on the platform glancing at my watch.

No sign of a train. I'm going to be late. A neat, anonymous man in a grey raincoat sits down next to me and says: 'Why do you rush from place to place? Your face is tense, you are thin and worried, you are driving yourself into the ground. Remember you only live twice. I used to rush around like you and I worked myself into an early grave. Then I took stock of myself, and since I returned to earth I have maintained a steady course. I learnt my lesson.'

29.8.1977   London: Smithfield Gardens, 11 a.m.

The moment when the clock struck; the sun burst through the clouds; the shadow of the statue with its pointing finger raced across the ground; the five pigeons stood poised in a line, each with its right foot raised; a shiver ran down the back of my neck before my eyes shut tight.

18.10.1977   London, EC1

The priest is walking to the grocery shop. He stops to have a few words with one of his parishioners, an old widow with a bandaged leg who stands at the edge of the pavement waiting to cross the road. He comforts her: 'Mrs Docherty, when all is said and done we are all worried about loose ends. The only difference between you and I is that you are probably worried about more loose ends than I am. I may be worried about two or three loose ends while you may be worried about four or five. Everyone in the world is worried about at least one loose end, in the end.' Mrs Docherty gazes blankly at his pink, smiling face. He pats her on the shoulder and continues on his way.

26.11.1977   London: The Odeon Cinema, Leicester Square, 10.45 a.m.

In the half-empty cinema usherettes with torches guide people to their seats. On screen, in a sleeper compartment of a train speeding through the night a youth crouches over a naked woman whom he has drugged with an injection from a hypodermic syringe. The youth unwraps a razor blade, lifts the woman's arm and slices through the veins on the inside of her wrist, fastening his lips to the wound as he hungrily drinks the spurting blood.

The man in the row in front of me arches backwards over his seat, his hands clenched between his legs, his breath sucked in through his clenched teeth.

12.20 p.m. a coffee bar in Leicester Square

I sat in this same seat two years ago this month. She sat in the seat on my left. It was after midnight. We talked about anything and everything to hide our nervousness, avoiding each other's eyes. We were falling in love. Now it seems that we are falling out, and we avoid each other's eyes out of fear, a fear of admitting that it might be going sour, curdling like milk which has been kept too long in the refrigerator. And I sit here staring at my coffee going cold like an actor in a bad film. It requires an effort of will to look out of the window.

12.25 p.m.

On one side of the alley is a Wimpy Bar: it looks exactly the same as any other Wimpy Bar anywhere in the country. I remember the one in Taunton in 1969, the 22nd of September to be exact. At a table at the rear of the restaurant a teenage girl in school uniform was being fed by her mother and father; they broke up the food on her plate and pushed it

62

gently into her mouth, waiting while she swallowed it before giving her any more. The girl ran her fingernails down the wall behind her.

On the other side of the alley is The Crystal Room, an 'amusement' centre filled with fruit machines. People stand in front of the machines, joylessly pulling the handles. The third machine from the left is the same as the one in my local pub. I remember a night in 1973 when the man in the grey suit seated by the fruit machine began to sway on his high stool. His eyes crossed and his face turned red. He ran his tongue around his lips, then, as if it had a will of its own, his tongue pushed out the corner of his mouth and up towards his nose. His elbow slipped off the bar and he crashed to the floor, bringing down the vase of plastic chrysanthemums on top of him. The back of his head slammed against the fruit machine, and I remember thinking at the time that if this were a comedy film he would hit the jackpot and glittering coins would come pouring out of the machine all over him, but all that happened was that whisky squirted out of his nostrils, then a man at a nearby table handed him his walking sticks and with the aid of two other men got him back onto his stool, then the barman set him up another drink. Having paused for a few moments everyone went back to their drinking. Tom, an enormous bloated man, leaned unsteadily against the bar, his eyes glazed. He began to bellow out an unrecognizable, tuneless song, Guinness running out of his wide open mouth onto his jacket. The barman watched him with a pained expression, saying: 'Tom, it's time you went back to work.' Tom was in charge of oxygen at the hospital round the corner.

At a table in the centre of the pub some lorry drivers were doing tricks with matches, none of which worked. One of the drivers was telling the others how on the way down he had hit a deer on the road, but it was not quite dead when he got out of the lorry so he sawed off its head with a hacksaw.

From her place at the bar Norah, the regular, carefully

watched the two new whores who were drinking with another group of drivers near the door. The taller of the two women had very short, receding hair, a white face, sunken cheeks, a pouting lipsticked mouth, a very prominent windpipe in her long neck, and a hunchback. Her companion was a dwarf; one of the lorry drivers was bouncing her on his knee.

At the far end of the bar was Sid, who always had a cold. Three times he reached for his drink and each time he withdrew his shaking hand. 'Come on Sid,' his neighbours said, 'you can do it old son.' 'All right, all right, just give me time that's all.' Sid also worked at the hospital.

12.35 p.m.

Alongside The Crystal Room is a cinema poster: a terrified man pursued by dogs. 'The Pack are hungry. When the familiar becomes the unknown.' I remember a day, a Sunday, about 15 years ago, I walked through the empty, terraced streets of my home town. Past the lace mills, across the canal, round the back of the railway sidings to the station, and bought a day return to one of the Derbyshire dales. The sun came out as soon as I got there; the air was sharp, it hurt my chest. I walked up the hill and I could see for miles. Two big hares ran across the open moorland ahead of me. I came to a dry-stone wall, climbed over and was immediately set upon by dozens of ferocious little dogs. The terriers were all around, biting at my ankles, tearing at my trousers and leaping high on either side as they tried to get at my face. Alerted by my shouts, the owner of the pack eventually appeared from behind his cottage and said: 'You shouldn't show them you're afraid, it only encourages them.'

2.12.1977   London: St John Street, EC1, 2.15 p.m.

A man looking at an advertising hoarding of a pair of thighs in black nylon stockings, smoke pouring out of the right-hand pocket of his overcoat.

14.12.1977   Croydon: Scarbrook Road, 11.55 a.m.

A bird-headed woman in a flesh-pink body stocking, with silver spoons fastened to her thighs, is having an epileptic fit on the floor of the school gymnasium.

1.3.1978   A restaurant in North London, 9.00 p.m.

Ian: 'A cup of coffee, please.'
Waitress: 'Certainly Sir.'
              Five minutes later
Waitress: 'Here you are, sir, one coconut ice cream.'
Ian: 'One what? I ordered a coffee.'
Waitress: 'A coffee? I'm terribly sorry sir.'
              Three minutes later
Waitress: 'Here you are, sir.'
Ian: 'What's this?'
Waitress: A Vesuvius, sir.'
Ian: 'A Vesuvius?'
Waitress: 'Yes sir, it's sponge soaked in Marsala wine, with vanilla, chocolate and Marsala ice cream, morello cherries, crushed meringue and fresh whipped cream. It's delicious, sir.'
Ian: 'I'm sure it is, but I ordered a coffee.'
Waitress: 'A coffee, sir? Oh, I'm so sorry.'
              Three minutes later
Waitress: 'Here you are sir: pot of tea for one.'

3.2.1978   Leeds: Merrion Centre, 10.23 a.m.

Two television sets side by side in a shop window: on one screen a pile of corpses in Auschwitz; on the other screen a smiling housewife putting a joint of pork into the oven. Behind one television set a shop assistant manicuring her nails; behind the other television set a man picking his teeth with a matchstick.

23.2.1978   Glasgow: St George's Square, 2.50 p.m.

A man playing a harmonica and walking along the pavement just too fast for people to put any coins in the cap which he holds in his outstreched hand.

Glasgow: Kelvingrove, 11.45 p.m.

The empty street glistening in the pouring rain. The sound of footsteps on the pavement of a side street. A television set in the window of a house facing onto the street; on screen a window through which can be seen the footprints of webbed feet; in the background a man clutching his throat, his eyes bulging.

10.3.1978   London

In the dentist's waiting room the patients sit smiling bravely. From the other side of the wall comes the whine of the electric drill. Through the half-open door of the surgery can be seen a woman's quivering legs stretched out in the chair. The door closes, then one minute later opens again. The dentist's assistant, a girl with coal-black hair and eyes, strides out of the surgery carrying a long-handled drain plunger. She smiles and says: 'There, that should do the trick.'

24.3.1978   Wales: Newport Station, 2.56 p.m.

The moment when: the guard blew his whistle; the fat woman
in the fur coat, like a mammoth, bent down and with her
gloved hand adjusted the plastic pants on the rear end of her
miniature poodle; the passenger in the train window slid his
tongue out between his lips into the left ear of the fashion
mannekin in the glass case on the platform on the other side of
the train carriage; the girl sitting on the platform bench,
dressed completely in black, groaned, leaned forward and
thrust her leather-gloved hand up the front of her sweater.

1.4.1978   London: Central Line tube train from Chancery
Lane to White City, 2.10 p.m.

The face of the woman in the opposite seat has a skin
complexion like a sugared almond. She wears a beautifully
cut grey tweed jacket and a grey pleated skirt. Her breasts stir
under her white silk blouse with the movement of the train.
Her eyes are glazed; they keep closing. Sleep overcomes her.
Her manicured hands slide off her lap, pulling back her skirt
over thighs in white silk stockings. Her face slackens; the little
frown disappears. Her lipsticked mouth parts to reveal pearly
white teeth on which, for a second, lands a black fly.

19.4.1978   Cardiff – London train, between Swindon and
Reading

By the side of the railway track: a man standing knee-deep in
manure, drinking tea from a white china cup, the saucer in his

left hand, the little finger of his right hand delicately cocked.

30.4.1978   London: Chapel Market, Islington, Sainsbury's supermarket, 12.15 p.m.

The holiday shopping is in full swing. Among the shelves of fizzy orange drinks, the baskets of pineapple chunks, the displays of tinned potatoes, the boxes of jellies, the piles of baked beans, the pyramids of meat balls, the bins of frozen chickens, the stacks of cheese crackers, the heaps of lard, the rows of pork pies and the racks of condensed milk, a man shuffles round the supermarket. He is dressed in a stiff and greasy suit, black boots and a dirty white roll-neck sweater the same colour as his face. At the throat, blood oozes through the wool of the sweater, adding to that which is already black and congealed. From him comes the purest smell of death, a stench so nauseating that shoppers turn away, gagging, holding their hands to their noses and mouths as they stare with strained concentration at the sponge mixtures. He moves like a ghost from shelf to shelf, filling his trolley with chicken, ham, bacon, potatoes, peas, carrots, syrup puddings and double cream; it seems that he has a good appetite.

7.5.1978   A hotel in Luton, 3.15 p.m.

In the darkened upper room above the bar people sit on chairs watching a white screen on which are being projected pictures of my Diary pages, which I am introducing: 'My Diary is not a first-person diary, it is a diary of description and observation. When my Diary moves from observation to speculation, it speculates on what might be now, what is on the other side of brick walls, on the other side of closed doors, on the other side of living-room curtains . . .'

From the other side of the door marked 'PRIVATE' alongside the cinema screen comes the sound of voices raised in furious anger: a man's voice, shrill and harsh; a woman's voice, hard and mean . . . YOU FUCKING LIAR! YOU BLEEDING ROTTEN LIAR! . . . DON'T YOU CALL ME A LIAR YOU TWO-FACED BASTARD! YOU STAND NEED TO TALK YOU BLOODY SHIT! . . . 'My Diaries record the side events of everyday life, by turns mundane' . . . YOU FUCKING ARSEHOLE! YOU BLEEDING SCUM! . . . 'curious' . . . YOU FILTHY TWO-FACED LYING SWINE! . . . 'bleak' . . . YOU SOD! . . . 'erotic' . . . YOU CUNT! . . . 'tender' . . . YOU SHIT-FACED RAT BAG! . . . 'vicious' . . . ARSEHOLES! . . . 'cunning' . . . YOU LYING SHIFTY FUCKER! . . . 'stupid' . . . YOU SNIVELLING CUNT-FACE! . . . 'ambiguous' . . . BOLLOCKS! . . . 'absurd' . . . YOU LYING FUCK-FACED POXY CUNT! . . . 'as observed by a personal witness.' From behind the door comes the sound of smashing crockery and shattering glass.

9.5.1978   Dog and Bull pub, Croydon, 1.35 p.m.

The bar is crowded with lunchtime drinkers. Beyond the bar counter is a doorway. Filling the door frame, on a wall beyond, is a large picture. A woman in a white dress, buttoned to the throat, has lifted the skirt of another woman who is bending forward over the back of a chair. The bending woman wears stockings to the knee, but no pants, and the woman in the white dress is stroking her left buttock with her right hand. Immediately in front of the table at which I sit two West Indian men are standing, drinking and conversing animatedly. The two black faces in profile frame the doorway and the picture contained within it; the visible outlines of the faces and the scene through the door merge. One mouth opens wide, the teeth gripping the wrist of the hand which is stroking the bending woman. The other face tilts forward, the nose pushed into the crevice between the buttocks, the nostrils flared. The chin of the other face tilts backwards, the goatee beard moving up the left leg of the bending woman. The tongue of the other face flicks out between the lips, over the right buttock of the bending woman, and touches for a moment the fingertips of the standing woman. A cigarette is lit, the flame from the match flaring up between the thighs of the bending woman, smoke rising from her buttocks.

12.5.1978   London: St John Street, EC1, 2.30 p.m.

A big fat woman in a yellow dress is standing with her back against a wall poster of a naked woman kneeling at the feet of a fashionably dressed young man who looks straight ahead as she clutches his immaculately trousered right leg and gazes up at him imploringly. The big fat woman stands placidly, holding her handbag in front of her. A businessman in a charcoal-grey pinstripe suit and carrying a briefcase, walks past. The woman erupts: 'AAAAAAARRRRRGGGHHH!!! YOU KNOW-ALL! YOU! YOU! YES YOU! LITTLE JOHNNY KNOW-ALL! YOU! YOU! YES, I KNOW THE LIKES OF YOU! AAAAAARRRRRGGGGHHH!' She springs forward, her eyes popping, her fist raised to strike him. He jumps back, steps aside, adjusts his bowler hat, and hurries across the road. She returns to stand silently in her previous position, holding her handbag in front of her.

14.5.1978   London: Smithfield Market, 4 a.m.

In the main meat market, among the thousands of hanging butchers' hooks, is a small dance floor. A uniformed police-man is dancing a slow, awkward waltz with a tiny woman in a long, white dress. Her face is level with the silver buckle on his belt; he holds her gingerly by the waist with his left hand, which also holds his helmet. On stage, against a pink tinselled backdrop, a fat middle-aged man in a pinstriped suit jacket and waistcoat, his trousers round his ankles, is crooning into the microphone.

15.5.1978   London: Farringdon Street, EC1, 10.10 a.m.

A meat porter is loading lumps of raw meat into the back of a taxi, under the watchful eyes of three nuns. The backseat of the taxi is filled up with legs of lamb, shoulders of pork, and beefsteaks. The nuns squeeze in amongst the meat and the taxi drives off.

21.5.1978   London: St John Street, EC1, 8.30 p.m.

On one side of the street: a procession of little girls in white Communion dresses. On the other side of the street: a woman in a white blouse and white trousers standing with her arms outstretched, her back against a wall poster of five grinning men standing in a line dressed in identical blue satin suits. In front of her: a man standing on the pavement with his trousers undone, waggling his prick at her.

25.7.1978   Ireland: the coast road from Cork to Rosslare, 6 p.m.

The storm which has raged for 12 hours has now reached its peak. The sea is boiling white. Huge waves crash against the shore. Torrential rain drives in from the sea across the open country. The roads are flooded, running like rivers. Cars and lorries with their headlights on full plough through the water, sending spray 15 feet into the air. At the head of the oncoming line of traffic is a Council Cleansing Department lorry sprinkling the road with water.

9 p.m.

Out at sea the storm is even worse. Force 8. The ferry boat pitches and rolls, sending glasses flying off the bar and upending old ladies, who lie on their backs among the smashed glasses and the pools of beer like overturned beetles with their legs waving feebly in the air. White-faced passengers lie in their own vomit on all the decks and stairs. Cheerful, gum-chewing members of the crew pick their way among the bodies collecting up the vomit bags which they had earlier distributed. Two crew members compare contents of bags:

'What's in yours then?'

'Looks like the Roast Chicken, Chips and Peas. What about you?'

'I reckon the King-Sized Hamburger, and Mixed Fruit Salad.'

3.8.1978   Glasgow

For the third successive day the drizzle falls ceaselessly. The city is grey and sodden in the permanent half-light. At 6.30 p.m. the city centre is already almost deserted. Three women stand glumly at a bus stop, clasping their handbags in front of themselves. A man on the opposite pavement walks into a lamp post. He staggers backwards, cursing quietly, sets off with elaborate determination and walks straight into the lamp post again. The women at the bus stop watch him dully; the drizzle is gradually soaking them. No sign of the bus.

24.8.1978   5.00 p.m. train from London to Honiton

The man in the opposite seat is a hunter. His face is strong
and suntanned. His hair short, greying, swept back. His
beard is black, flecked with grey, neatly trimmed. His suit is
blue-grey. In the top pocket of his jacket two fountain pens
are clipped. His socks are dark blue with a pale blue stripe.
His shoes are brown suede. At regular intervals he draws back
his left shirt cuff to check the time on his golden watch. He
tightens his blue tie, on the front of which is embroidered a
hunt motif just prior to the kill. He carefully puts into his
mouth a white peppermint between fingernails which are
filed to sharp points.

2.9.1978   Leeds: Modelia Fashion Shop, Boar Lane,
3.10 p.m.

A woman in the shop window, her right hand inside the
unbuttoned skirt of a fashion mannequin, her left cheek
pressed against the mannequin's shoulder, her eyes closed,
her lips parted, the head of the mannequin turned away, its
gaze fixed haughtily on the street outside the window.

20.9.1978   London: St John Street, EC1, 9.55 a.m.

On the white line in the middle of the road, between the two
streams of traffic, are two eels.

28.9.1978   London: Gerry Cottle's Circus, North Mill Fields, E5, 8.30 p.m.

In the centre of the circus ring: a bed with a man and a dwarf in it under the covers; on the bedside table, a candle which is moving rhythmically up and down in its holder; in the front row of the ringside seats, a young girl with her left hand between her legs and her right index finger working up and down her right nostril.

2.10.1978   London: The Cut, SE1, 3.15 p.m.

On the pavement of the busy street: a woman sitting on a public wall in front of a public bush set in a brick base. With the index finger and thumb of her kid-gloved right hand she is extracting a hair from her little sandwich. In the bush, among the foliage: a calloused, hairy hand and a prick from which comes a stream of piss. Steam rises from the bush.

26.10.1978   London to Maidstone train, 12.45 p.m.

The businessman in the pinstriped suit is reading, behind his *Daily Telegraph*, the latest issue of *Raunchy* magazine; he is engrossed in an article entitled 'A Bit On The Side'. His brow is furrowed, his chin sunk into his chest; the breath from his nostrils has steamed up his gold tiepin. The train reaches Swanley. The station loudspeaker announces that the train will divide here and the passengers for Maidstone East should travel in the front four coaches. The businessman hurriedly stuffs the magazine into his briefcase, gathers up his mackintosh and umbrella, and struggles out of the door with difficulty as he is experiencing acute problems with his trousers. Bent almost double, his face the colour of a tomato, he shuffles along the platform towards the front four coaches, watched with interest by a group of schoolgirls sitting on a platform bench who blow pink gum bubbles as he passes by.

31.10.1978   London: Cowcross Street, EC1, 11.30 p.m.

The lamplit street is filled with acrid smoke which pours out of a soot-encrusted opening in the steel wall of the bacon factory. The pavement is littered with offal and lumps of fat. In the doorway of the bacon factory, alongside a window filled with boneless hams, a man and a woman are embracing, his left leg pushed between her thighs, her fingers in his hair, his lips moving up her neck. The bacon smoke settles round them like a fog.

24.12.1978   London

It's Christmas. The city settles under a carpet of vomit: on the pavements and window ledges; on public benches, doorsteps, stairs and landings; up the sides of bus stops; down the sides of lamp posts; at the foot of walls; in window-boxes and at the base of potted shrubs; on carpets, rugs and the seats of chairs; down blouses, shirt fronts, lapels, sleeves and trouser legs; in sinks, lavatory bowls, drinking fountains, beards, hair, eyes and noses; dripping down between the branches of the Christmas tree. Proof of a good time.

5, 6, 7, 8, 9.1.1979   Belfast

Steel gates. Steel fences. Steel bars. Barred windows. Shuttered windows. Burnt-out buildings. Bombed-out pubs. Oil drums filled with concrete line the pavements.

Vans cruise the streets, two men in the front behind bullet-proof glass; two men in the back with loaded rifles sticking out of the rear doors. Men with guns stand in shop doorways against backgrounds of cream crackers, baked beans, bacon, doughnuts, shirts, socks, nylon stockings and front-fastening bras. Periodically one of the men lifts his rifle and takes aim.

A ritualized, monotonous round. Walk don't run. Don't point. Don't wave. Don't shout across the street. A steady pace. Eyes skinned.

Checkpoint. Arms up. Arms out on either side. Legs apart. Open coat. Close coat. Proceed.

Such a clean city. No rubbish on the pavements. No refuse in the gutters. No plastic rubbish sacks outside the shops.

Complete streets of bricked-up windows and doorways covered with corrugated iron. Some buildings completely encased in steel cages, inside which business continues.

In every parked car sits someone staring blankly through the window.

Take care. Think twice. Look up. Fix a time. Leave word. Parents, check your children.

Habitual. Routine. Normal.

15.1.1979   London, 6–8 p.m.

Dialogue for the cocktail hour:

'Hello, how are you?'
If I had a gun I would shoot myself.
'Not so bad, how are you?'

'Hello, how are you?'
My head is full of ants.
'O.K. How's yourself?'

'Hello, how are you?'
As if plaster of Paris had been injected under my skin.
'Much the same. And you?'

'Hello. Are you well?'
I can hardly breathe.
'In the pink. What about you?'

'Howyoudoing?'
Desperate.
'Fineandyou?'

'O.K.?'
Demented.
'O.K.'

'All right?'
At my wits end.
'All right.'

'Pleased?'
You could never understand in a thousand years.
'Reasonably, you know me.'

'Keeping busy?'
All day I stared at the wall.
'Can't complain. And you?'

'Winning?'
Lost everything.
'Breaking even.'

'Hello, how are you, where's it all happening?'
If I knew I wouldn't tell you.
'Fine. Over there maybe.'

'Hello! Long time no see! How are you?'
Your limp hand sets my teeth on edge.
'Never been better. How are you?'

'Hello, how's things?'
Your little smile makes me want to push your teeth down
your throat.
'Oh, you know, win some lose some.'

'Hello! How are you? Nice to see you!'
Please don't embrace me or I'll vomit.
'Fine, fine.'

'Hi! Glad you could come. How are you?'
I could spit in your face.
'Be better for a drink.'

'Hi there! Good to see you! How's tricks?'
My God what a snivelling little shit you are.
'Looking up, how about you?'

'Hello. Everything O.K.?'
I could turn a flame-thrower on you all.
'Not bad, not bad.'

'Hello, how are you?'
You sod. You sod. You fucking sod.
'So so, and you?'

'Hello, how are you? You look a bit tired.'
Tired, yes. A lethargy that is in the marrow of the bones.
An ache that is in the nerves of the eyes. A congestion in the
ears that blocks out all sound except that inside the head. The
cheeks sucked in by fear. Hands shaking. Legs sandbagged. A
despair that is in the roots of the teeth.

'A bit tired, yes, it's been a long day.'

'Hello, how are you?'
I want to hold you in my arms until we both gasp for breath. I want to kiss you all over. To hold your hair in my hands with my fingertips against your scalp. To run through the streets with you hand in hand. I want us to laugh, cry, whisper and shout all at the same time together.
'Oh, same as ever. How are you?'

'How are you?'
Who are you?
'Getting by, and you?'

20.1.1979   Paris: Métro Concorde, 10.10 a.m.

A man gripping a briefcase, his fists clenched, his teeth bared, rocking backwards and forwards on his heels, his face each time nearer the face of the man on the advertising hoarding who has been hit in the eye with a snowball and who is rocked back on his heels, his teeth bared, his fists clenched.

14.3.1979   A multi-storey office block in central London, 2.40 p.m.

Two men are walking along a corridor, each absorbed in reading the document in his hand; they reach the open door to the office exactly side by side and in step and jam themselves in the doorway.

17.3.1979   London: St John Street, EC1, 11.59 a.m.

A man in a pinstriped business suit, white shirt, blue tie, polished brogues, running full tilt down the street, his arms outstretched in pursuit of eight shrieking teenaged girls.

13.4.1979   Cardiff, 10.05 a.m.

An old man in a flat cap, with a chest problem, stands bent over on the pavement, the fingers of both hands on each side of his nose from which the string of green snot hangs down to the ground. Behind him is an advertising hoarding on which is pictured a large brown ball of meat, dripping juice, impaled on a fork, beneath the caption: 'It's Brains you need.'

6.5.1979   London, 11.40 p.m.

A whining, slurred voice comes over the airwaves, sniffing and sucking his teeth between words:

'This is Back Street Radio' – sniff – 'broadcasting on 226 metres, right?' – suck – 'We play music.' – sniff – 'Sometimes.' – sniff – 'But first I want to say hello to Jill.' – sniff – 'Hello Jill, I want you to come round to where I'm broadcasting from, you know where it is, allright?' – suck – 'Here's a good record.' – sniff – 'Here's a good 'un' – sniff – 'What the fuck is it? I can't see. It's going round and round. Never mind it's a good one.' – suck – 'Oh Christ, I've scratched it.' – sniff – 'Come on, start you fucker.' – suck – 'If I whack this thing it should work.' – whack – 'Right, here we go.' – mmm – 'Shit, now it's distorting. The turntable's fucked.' – sniff – 'What I'd give for a mixer. But, see, we have to have the microphone turned up full, because if we turn it down we're not audible, see?' – suck – 'Oh well, this is Back Street Radio here.' – sniff – 'Jill, hello, I want you to come round, O.K.? Come on round please.' – sniff – 'Tell you something though, if you want a drink don't go to the Tufnell Park Tavern, the beer's lousy and they shout at you to piss off at closing time. Fucking rude I think. Go to the Admiral instead, that's a good one. That's why I'm in the state I'm in.' – suck – 'Oh Christ, I need a piss.' – sniff – 'Jill, please come round, come on Jill you know where I am.' – suck – 'This is Back Street Radio on 226 metres.' – sniff – 'Now, where were we?' – sniff – 'Fuck knows.' – suck – 'Anyway, here's track five, whatever that is.' – sniff – 'Jill, why don't you come round?' – sniff – 'Or I'll come round there.' – suck – 'Where's all the fucking records gone then? Who's had them? I bet it was Trevor, the sod. Hang about.' – sniff – 'This is Back Street Radio you're listening to.' – suck – 'Jill, I think your tits are fantastic. I wish you'd come round.' – sniff – 'This bloody record's all warped, I can't play this.' – suck – 'Jill, I sincerely hope you're tuned in.' – sniff – 'Oh shit, I just trod on the turntable. That's screwed it.' – suck – 'Jill, I hope to Christ you've got a radio.' – sniff – 'This is Back Street Radio here and the only record we've got left is warped and I've really fucked up the turntable.' – suck – 'If I could only work out how to use this fucking thing we'd be all right.' – sniff – 'If only.' – suck – sniff – 'Shit.' – sniff – 'Oh fuck it, I've had enough of this. Jill, I'm coming round.' – sniff.

2.6.1979   London

The clock across the river said 5.07 p.m. I walked down the steps and into the cinema. On screen was a hotel bedroom. A trussed and gagged man lay on the floor. The cupboard door was open. Two eyes peered from under the bed. The clock on the wall behind the bed said 5.10 p.m., as did my watch.

6.6.1979   Vienna, 11.30 a.m.

On the streets the heat was suffocating. In the catacombs the chill corridors led one into another like a maze. Jesus, stripped to the waist, lay with his spine arched across the thighs of his anguished mother, his right hand hanging limp, the fingertips of his left hand touching his crotch. Through the iron grille the walls of the room were built of human femurs with skulls jammed in between. The floor was heaped with bones. The suntanned girl shivered, pulled down her white vest and hugged herself as she climbed the iron staircase up into the sunshine. The paving stones were hot beneath the feet. A trembling boy lay on the ground. A policewoman crouched over him, her white blouse open. Tourists sat gaping. Mournful white horses stood around the square. A small girl lifted up her dress. The boy on the ground was shaking. Two lovers on a bench slid their tongues in and out of each others' mouths.

30.7.1979   London: Barclays Bank, West Smithfield, 2.05 p.m.

A man with blood on his boots is staring through the glass panel between him and the raven-haired cashier who is flicking through the pile of banknotes with her wetted fingertip, while the clerk leans over her shoulder from behind, staring at the paying-in slips by her left hand at the same time as he runs his tongue along the rim of her collar.

3.8.1979   London: Lord's Cricket Ground, Second Test Match between England and India

The sun is shining. The grass is green. Spectators from all over the country have made an early start, found their seats and settled in. Picnic hampers are opened up, bottles and flasks uncorked. At 3 p.m. the sky turns black as ink. There is thunder and lightning followed by a torrential downpour. A deluge. The ground staff emerge wearing sou'westers, oilskin capes and wellington boots; they wheel the covers onto the wicket and lay plastic sheets over the surrounding area. The rain comes down like steel rods. Spectators sit under the stands eating cucumber sandwiches and drinking tea; they stare intently at the cricket ground, which gradually becomes a lake. A mother says to her son: 'They say it might clear up later.' One of the covers floats away. Two men in suits and wellington boots, carrying umbrellas, wade out to the middle, peer under the remaining wicket cover, then wade back to the pavilion where the lights shine brightly, silhouetting the club members who stand on the balcony sipping gin and tonics. Above them is the BBC radio box in which the commentators sit behind microphones commentating. Over by the Tavern Stand the spectators are singing in unison; three of them make their way to the middle of the ground and play an imaginary game of cricket: one the 'batsman', one the 'bowler', one the 'umpire'. The 'bowler' bowls the imaginary ball, the 'batsman' swings to leg and the 'umpire' gives him out; there is a deafening crack of thunder directly above and all three fall flat on their backs in the water. There is a generous round of applause from the crowd. Lightning streaks overhead. A man, naked except for a pair of blue underpants, dives off the boundary railings and executes a scrappy breaststroke, then sinks. In the Gentlemen's Lavatory behind the Mound Stand the murky water draining from the ground runs through like a river, lapping round the ankles of the men who stand urinating into each individual porcelain stall, staring up at the white tiles as others stand waiting their turn.

26.12.1979   Tenby, Pembrokeshire, 10.30 a.m.

The POSSIBLE AIR SEA RESCUE has been advertised on posters around the town for several weeks, and now crowds line the promenade and cliff tops above the North Beach, waiting stoically in the pouring rain. Out at sea a man sits in a small boat, possibly in difficulties. Punctually at 10.30 a.m. a Royal Navy helicopter hovers over the appointed spot. The man in the boat below waves his arms. The helicopter flies away. Muffled applause from the crowds as they clap with mittened hands.

1.3.1980   London: Fann Street, EC1, 11.50 a.m.

An ashen-faced man leaning against a lamp post while a flock of pigeons at his feet gobble up the pool of steaming vomit.

3.4.1980   London: The Pavement, Clapham Common, SW4

Good Friday eve. Two adjacent posters: Jesus hangs on the cross, looking balefully down on an advertisement for Public Liability Insurance Policies.

21.4.1980   London: Smithfield Gardens, EC1, 2.20 p.m.

A blue-rinsed woman brings her giant poodle into the gardens. She carries a bag of bread for the birds. She scatters the bread cubes upon the ground. The birds hover overhead, squawking and twittering while the poodle greedily eats up the bread and the woman stands with feet apart, vainly pointing her finger and shouting: 'Heel Jason! Heel!' Jason gobbles all the bread and shits on the daffodils.

1.6.1980   London: Waterlow Park

The brass band finishes its programme and takes a bow, then plays the national anthem as the audience stand to attention beside their deckchairs. The bandleader salutes. In front of the teahouse near the bandstand families sit in the sunshine at small tables, drinking tea and eating little cakes, the family dogs lying at their feet. A bull terrier growls at an Old English sheepdog. Another bull terrier snaps at a corgi. A dogfight breaks out. Within seconds six dogs are snarling and biting at each other in a furious, writhing heap. Cups of tea are spilled in laps. Cakes fly out of hands. Tables are overturned. Children are knocked down. Women start screaming. Men begin kicking and shouting at the dogs. A man grabs a bull terrier by the back legs and hurls it across the lawn. The bull terrier's owner hits the man on the jaw with a right uppercut. Dogs and people fight among the flowerbeds.

19.6.1980   Lord's Cricket Ground: Second Test Match, England *v*. West Indies

Unseasonal weather. Grey clouds move across the sky, driven by a bitter wind. The cricketers, cocooned in woollens, hop up and down rubbing their hands. The spectators sit hunched up against the cold, swathed in coats and scarves, their hands cupped around the hot drinks from their thermos flasks. The paralysed blind man stares sightlessly through his dark glasses, his plastic mac buttoned up to his neck, his cap jammed firmly on his head. His fingers grip the arms of his wheelchair, his ears twitch, his nostrils flare as he sniffs the wind, and he licks his lips with keen anticipation as he awaits the start of a new over. The sun breaks through the clouds and he lifts his face upwards. He says: 'But why doesn't he move fine leg deeper?'

6.10.1980

From Cambridge to Broxbourne the railway runs through pleasant, low-lying countryside; cows and sheep graze in the fields, herons fish beside the lakes and streams. From Broxbourne to Liverpool Street the urban sprawl takes over, and the factory walls alongside the track are painted with hundreds of slogans welcoming the traveller back to the big city: WOG SCUM. NIGGER SHIT. BLACK BASTARDS. KILL WOGS. BURN NIGGERS. WELCOME TO NIGGER SHIT SLUMLAND.

6.11.1980   Cambridge: 12.45 a.m.

For the past few days and nights there has been a young man sitting in a cage on the lawn in front of the chapel, directly across the street from my flat. He is protesting about the plight of political prisoners around the globe, including Siberia. The icy-cold weather at least gives his vigil a touch of realism. In the early hours of this morning two earnest young men engaged in a progressively more heated debate about the degrees of physical mistreatment suffered by political prisoners; they eventually settled the argument by punching each other in the middle of the road, while the lone protester sat glumly shivering in his cage.

17.11.1980   Cambridge

Seven students sit around a table in the bar. One is dressed in cavalry-twill trousers, white shirt, cravat and striped blazer; he is concerned that his friend, who is sitting on his left similarly dressed except that his blazer is blue flannel, arrives on time for rowing practice at 7 a.m. the following morning, whereas his friend is arranging the details of the following night's party with the girl on his left whose tracksuit has become torn through continuous jogging so that it exposes her white inner thigh. On her left a girl with close-cropped hair, baggy dungarees and three badges is planning with the girl on her left, who wears a pink Fiorucci boiler suit, the protest they intend to make the next day outside Woolworths against their special offers on deodorized tampons, while the youth sitting next to her who has a prison-crop hairstyle, three-day stubble, stained sweatshirt, faded jeans and plastic shoes, discusses the merits of Tottenham Hotspurs' back four with the girl on his left who is dressed in a tweed skirt, white blouse and cashmere sweater and is convinced that her old flatmate is the Yorkshire Ripper. Each student speaks in the same accent, tone and level of voice.

5.12.1980   Carlisle

I have been here for a week making two videotapes. Away from the cloisters and the dreaming spires the shock of returning to the north of England is like a cold bath. Cobbled

87

streets. Mean, cramped terrace houses. Closed factories. Perms and chips. Pinched, sallow faces. Cambridge seemed a world away. But on the train coming back I found in the litter bin in the toilet the Christmas issue of *Knave*: three pages stuck together, middle page spread torn out. The correspondence section contained a letter from one 'A.S. of Cambridge' in response to a letter in a previous issue from 'Pamela, of West Yorkshire' extolling the virtues and sensual delights of wet clothing. A.S. would like to see Pamela in 'a neat suit, hat, gloves, blouse, bra, panties, stockings, suspenders, boots and handbag, being subjected joyously to bucketfuls of warm water'. I wonder who A.S. is, and whether he and Pamela will ever meet? It seems that bridges could in fact be built between the north and south. A.S. would also like to see more slapstick enlivening these joyless times, scenes in which 'all hell breaks loose, with all kinds of pies and liquids being hurled through the air and landing squarely in the faces and on the clothes of very beautiful women, who retaliate with more of the same'.

Christmas 1980   Wales

In the evening: on the television screen is the epic film *The Towering Inferno*. The multi-storey tower block is engulfed in roaring flames and wracked by deafening explosions which blast the trapped inhabitants through the plate-glass windows into space to crash to their deaths on the pavements far below. On the other side of the living room an open fire burns merrily within the grate, slightly larger than the inferno contained within the television screen.

5.1.1981   London, in the pub

The men with hard, slim-line executive briefcases and soft, swollen bellies stood in a circle around the table they had cleared of glasses and rummaged around in their open flies and swayed from side to side and guffawed and slapped each other on the back and smacked their fists into the palms of their hands and one of them fell over onto the floor.

The three men huddled around the gas fire rubbed their hands and wrists and puffed out their cheeks and agreed that the fucking cunt was not worth a fucking toss and he could rot in hell as far as they were concerned and all agreed that if they'd got the cunt back in Armagh they'd know how to settle the fucking bastard. And the landlord said: 'Shhh, gentlemen please, this is a respectable house.'

7.1.1981   Cambridge

Written message found in a telephone box: 'Norman, your prayer partnership this week is with Arun.'

29.5.1981   Cambridge, 10.45 a.m.

In the forecourt of Peterhouse a marquee has been erected for the visit today by the Queen. The red carpet is being laid out from the pavement to the marquee. The carpet has to pass over a small area of cobblestones; two workmen are filling in the gaps between the cobbles with sand and levelling it so that there is no possibility of an uneven surface beneath the carpet which might cause the high-heeled Queen to totter. Inside the marquee more workmen are wrapping the tent poles with white bandages in case the royal shoulder should brush against them.

9.6.1981   Cambridge, students talking:

'Roger's playing tennis, Simon's playing squash, Tristram's at the demo, Sarah's on the river, Rupert's gone down to London to get his hair cut.'

10.6.1981   Cambridge: The Locomotive pub, Mill Road

'Pint of bitter, please.'

Through the gap between the first and second buttons of the shirt of the man standing next to me a small green snake puts out its head, flicks its tongue then slides back inside the shirt.

'And a box of matches.'

9.7.1981   Cambridge

An Irish pub in a back street away from the main tourist routes. The bar is run down and decrepit. Two pool tables. Carrolls All Ireland All Stars poster alongside the dartboard. Framed portrait of John F. Kennedy over the bar next to the sign saying, 'Last Paddy served at 11 p.m.'

Waiting for my turn to come up on the pool table, I'm sitting in a corner reading *Melmoth The Wanderer*. The Irishman at the next table says: 'What's the book?' '*Melmoth The Wanderer*'. 'Is it a good book?' 'It's a very good book.' 'What's it about?' I describe the first few chapters wherein young John Melmoth is called from Trinity College, Dublin, to inherit the family seat in County Wicklow and is then haunted by an ancestor, Melmoth The Wanderer, who has sold his soul to the devil in return for prolonged life. My neighbour sinks his Guinness, and after a long pause says: 'Aye, they're all fucking wanderers in Wicklow.'

16.8.1981   8.36 a.m. train from Liverpool Street to Cambridge

It is a glorious summer morning. The lakes and streams alongside the railway track sparkle in the sunlight. Opposite me is a Chinaman eating dried plums. Across the aisle are a Frenchman and woman, both reading *Grande Bretagne* guidebooks. I am reading a newspaper article on the aerodynamics of off-spin bowling. The train comes to a halt. The footplateman, a teenage youth whose face is ashen, hurries along the aisle from the front of the train. He blurts out: 'There's been an accident . . . just walked in front of the train . . . going to be a delay . . . Oh God.' He gets out of the train and waits for the guard who is laying warning detonators on the opposite track. The Frenchman glances at his wristwatch, lights a menthol cigarette and taps his fingers on the table top.

The Chinaman finishes the last of his plums and goes to sleep. Two sweating policemen struggle through the gravel alongside the track. 'Mummy, mummy I want to do a wee-wee!' 'Shh, something's happened.' The delay provides a welcome distraction for two youths, one with long hair, kaftan and shades, the other crew-cut and leather-clad, who have previously been drifting aimlessly up and down the train, half-heartedly pestering girls. The leather boy, announcing that he's going to have a look at the body, climbs out of the train and sets off down the track, carrying his cassette player which blares out Adam and the Ants. A businessman in a pinstriped suit leans out of the window and with binoculars observes the activities of the police in the distance as they measure and mark around the white shrouded bundle in between the tracks. Soon everyone goes back to their seats and their reading, eating, knitting, and eventually the train continues its journey to Cambridge.

'British Rail wishes to apologize to passengers for the late arrival of this train, which was caused by operating difficulties.'

November 1981 Cambridge

The prospective next tenant of my flat, an American woman, came round unannounced to view it while I was finishing my breakfast. I showed her round and filled in all the details. She didn't like the way the landing separated the living room from the bathroom and kitchen, and she didn't like the kitchen, but she didn't intend using it anyway she said because she never cooked. She thought the living room was rather small and the carpet did not have a very thick pile. She was sure the flat would be cold. I said it was the warmest flat I had ever lived in. She thought the bed looked too soft and might be bad for her back. I said it was the most comfortable bed I had ever slept in. She thought there would be a separate bedroom. I said I was afraid there wasn't. She asked what were the arrangements for cleaning and laundry. I said, 'No problem, dust and mop the floors every now and then, clean the windows inside, and take the laundry over to the King's launderette, the cheapest in town; it's a cinch.' Her mouth dropped open in genuine shock: 'You mean I would be expected to do those things myself? Oh no, I couldn't possibly, I wouldn't know how. I would have to have a bedmaker, a cleaner and a laundress.' I said: 'You mean you've never done any of those things?' She said: 'Why no, I never have while I've been in Cambridge, and before I came here I was in Africa and always had local servants.' She must have seen the expression on my face, for she quickly added: 'You see, over there they are so inexpensive.'

5.1.1982   London: St John Street, EC1

The man stumbling through the snow slid to the ground. He struggled to his feet and immediately fell on his face. He crawled up on his hands and knees, stood up, swayed, and fell backwards. He lay on his back in the snow, his arms waving feebly until, exhausted, he was still and the snow settled on him. The pedestrians on the opposite pavement resumed their journey to the bus stop.

8.1.1982   London, in the pub

Half the customers were spooning jellied eels, the others were eating bagels. A fat man walked in on his knees, his mouth filled with half-chewed bread; he hauled himself to his feet and fell on the neck of the man slumped unconscious in the corner seat.

'I want to give him a French kiss with food in my mouth,' said the fat man, three times, sodden lumps of bread dropping from his lips onto his bulging stomach which had burst the buttons of his shirt.

9.1.1982   London, in the pub

It was freezing cold. A priest sat in front of the fire, blocking off the heat. He was recounting his car crash and how he went through the car roof and landed exactly 39 feet further up the road. God saved him from certain death. He kept talking and talking and then he began to sing. I couldn't take any more. 'Shut up will you!' I shouted, 'for Christ's sake!' The priest smiled benignly. A man walked past on his way to the gents and sneezed. 'Bless you my son,' said the priest.

16.1.1982   London, in the pub

Man in the gents lavatory furiously pulling the coins returned lever of the contraceptive machine, without success. Punches the machine. 'Bollocks, I didn't want to fuck the bitch anyway.'

25.1.1982   Back home to Derbyshire

In the pub the same people in the same chairs at the same tables having the same argument. As if time had stood still.

'Hello Uncle Arthur.'

'Eyup Ian, pint of Pedigree is it? Trevor's only this minute gone, you just missed him. Ey, but he's a right one, he don't improve. Have I seen you since he brought them chickens round? I was sitting watching "Coronation Street", I was just dozing off when there was a knock on the window. Rap-rap-rap! I said to our Doris, who the bloody hell's that at this time of night? It were Trevor. He says, "Arthur you know you said you wouldn't mind a chicken if I ever had one spare, well I've got 2,000 in the lorry outside, how many do you want?" Bogger me if they weren't all alive, and there's me still with my slippers on neck-holing them in the dark while Trevor holds the flashlight. Thought I was going to have a quiet night and there I was strangling chickens on the pavement. You never heard such a row. So after a bit I said to Trevor that's enough, there'll be no more room in the pantry. Took me a month to pluck the boggers.'

The same story every time. Third year of telling. I know every word. Man at the next table staring at his pint: 'My beer at home's not ready, else I'd have stayed in.'

9.2.1982   Newport, Wales: the indoor market

Three brown doors: one labelled GENTLEMEN, one labelled LADIES, one labelled TROUT.

10.2.1982   Newport railway station, 5.45 p.m.

A youth and his girlfriend sit in adjoining seats in the buffet. She puts her arm round his neck and kisses him. A man on the other side of the buffet puts down his sausage roll, rushes across and punches her in the back.

12.2.1982   London: St John Street, EC1

A man carrying a polythene bag full of tongues sits down at the café table alongside a woman who is scratching her leg. A man walks past the window with the headless carcase of a deer on his shoulders. On the other side of the street the second-floor window of the Dream City Massage Parlour For Men is raised and a slender hand with long red fingernails slips through the gap between the curtains and flicks the ash from a cigarette out onto the street below where a man with his trousers round his ankles is shitting in a doorway.

5.10.1982   London: St John Street, EC1, 10.30 a.m.

An old man walking along the pavement gradually takes shorter steps until he is only making progress an inch at a time. Eventually his legs refuse to move at all despite his frantic efforts, and he falls onto his back where he lies helpless. Passers by pass by. A muscular young man with his left leg in a plaster cast comes bowling along on crutches at great speed, clearing the fallen man with one deft leap as he rushes to catch the bus.

16.10.1982 London

To get to my studio in Wapping I cycle through the Grand Avenue of the Central Markets, go round the back of St Barts along Little Britain and King Edward Street, then left up Angel Street onto St Martin's Le Grand, through the City down Cheapside and Poultry past the Mansion House, past the Bank along Cornhill and Leadenhall Street, then cut across the junction of Aldgate and Jewry Street onto the Minories.

This morning the route is lined with crowds awaiting the arrival of the massed ranks of the armed forces who will march to the Mansion House in celebration of our glorious victory in the Falkland Islands. The Royal Navy, the Merchant Navy, the Royal Marines, the Royal Artillery, the Guards, the Paratroopers and the Royal Air Force will come marching round the corner any moment now to the strains of 'Those Magnificent Men In Their Flying Machines' and other assorted tunes.

I am delayed by traffic lights directly outside the Mansion House. I gaze at the pavement full of faces. Grey, mean faces, young and old. Mums and dads and the children with the day off school. Old soldiers and City workers taking an early lunch. Shoulder to shoulder in their macs in the drizzle, waving their little sodden flags.

A small corner, out of the limelight, has been set aside for five token war cripples: a concession by the Lord Mayor in response to newspaper criticism of his original decision not to invite any of the wounded 'because they might be embarrassed'. The chosen five sit spick and span in their wheelchairs with their uniformed military nurses standing behind them. No sign of the other legless and armless, the blind, deafened and brain-damaged, the scarred, burnt, mutilated and disfigured. Just five clean-cut young men with their fresh-faced, permed nurses. Out of sight out of mind. Either you die a hero or Johnny comes marching home again.

> You haven't an arm and you haven't a leg,
> Hurroo, hurroo.
> You haven't an arm and you haven't a leg,
> Hurroo.
> You haven't an arm and you haven't a leg,
> You eyeless, noseless, chickenless egg,
> You'll have to be put in a bowl to beg,
> Johnny I hardly knew you.*

With their drums and guns and guns and drums and their Rapier missiles on rubber wheels.

Then the lights turn to amber and I pedal as fast as I can down Cornhill.

Damned bike. Go faster! Past the leering devils with pendulous breasts and forked scaly tails on the roof above the Cornhill Men's Fashion Shop. Past the gruesome Tower. Past the grey elephants with white tusks guarding the entrance to Ivory House. Then out past the Royal Mint along the Highway and through the docks to Wapping, where it's damp and quiet. The big iron door to the warehouse clangs shut and all sound is cut off.

My studio is on the third floor of this Victorian dockside warehouse. The background music from my radio is overlaid with the sound of the military flypast. I can see the aeroplanes from my studio window as they move in formation over Wapping and towards the City. First the helicopters: the Wasps, Sea Kings, Gazelles and Chinooks. The Victor

* Traditional Irish ballad.

tankers flanked by Sea Harrier jet fighters. Finally, three V-formations of Vulcan bombers, Nimrods and Hercules transport aircraft. The sense of foreboding and ugly, heavy menace is somehow heightened by their unnaturally slow speed as they parade for the gawping crowds below.

26.2.83   Cambridge: Green Street, 1.40 p.m.

On the pavement on one side of the street a young woman in a red coat with a white lace petticoat showing below the hem is standing watching a sticky rubber octopus moving down the inside of a plate-glass shop window. On the pavement on the other side of the street a man in a white laboratory coat is crouched down beside a big black dog, both staring at the woman on the opposite pavement. The man carefully strokes the dog's ears and neck and the dog's glistening red prick emerges like a wax crayon from the black hair surrounding it.

11.3.1983   London: West Smithfield, 2 p.m.

In the foreground a newspaper placard: DEARER TEETH.
   In the background a sobbing woman.
   Around the corner a man with his hands in his overcoat pockets, his shoulders shaking with mirth.

4.4.1983   Tenby, Pembrokeshire, Easter Monday

The bright sun of early spring shines down on the blue sea which washes gently onto the shore of the harbour in which fishing boats bob at anchor against a backdrop of white, pink and blue-painted houses and hotels. A lone child on the beach is collecting shells. Beyond the red lifeboat station at the head of the slipway the statue on the emerald-green headland stands grey against the sky. Seagulls soar overhead. Out at sea a cormorant skims over the waves beneath the arc of a rainbow. In Woolworths the holidaymakers stand with their hands thrust into the pockets of their quilted anoraks, watching a television screen on which is a picture of a seaside harbour in which boats bob at anchor beneath whirling seagulls, while out at sea a water-skier skims across the waves.

11.4.1983   Moving to Norwich

Met Stan with his van at 8 a.m. It took an hour to get to my studio in Wapping and another hour to get out of town. Traffic jams everywhere: half the city cordoned off because of a Second World War bomb they had dredged out of the Thames. Drove to Norwich along the Mll. Torrential rain swept across the fens. The truck leaked like a sieve.

Stan is a jack of all trades with the eternal optimism of the born chancer. He comes from a background of villains, hooligans and con-artists. He continually tells stories as we drive along . . .

'Dolly Parton? Now there's a woman. Bleeding hell, what a cracker. My mate Marty's potty about her. He's got his truck done up with steers horns sticking out on either side of the cab and 'Dolly Parton's Number One Worldwide Fan' in letters across the windscreen. Flies over to Nashville to see her shows and soon as she comes on stage he whips his shirt off to show his tattoo of her on his back.'

'Cricket? No it doesn't agree with me. See, when I was a kid I was watching a game on a Sunday afternoon in the park near our house. And this geezer who was batting gives the ball a whack, right? Sails over the boundary and hits me smack in the eye. Wallop! So I staggers off home, eye closing up and when I got home I go into the living room, only got one eye,

99

can't see where I'm going, and trip over the fucking carpet and put my hand in the fire! Still got the scars. No. don't mind watching the cricket on the telly, I just don't like standing near it – that's all.'

'See the fight the other night? A draw was the last result I expected. But a classic, no doubt about it, boxer against puncher. Now my brother he was no boxer, in fact he couldn't stand 'em. He could have made the grade if he hadn't been so impatient. See, he'd be up against a boxer, some little sod going tap, tap, tap, dancing round him sticking little jabs on the end of his nose, not hurting him like but annoying him, piling up the points. And sure as day he'd think sod this and lose his rag, put an arm lock round the little fucker's neck and smash him, or grab him by the shoulders and nut him, or kick him in the balls. He knocked out one guy clean as a whistle while he was getting up off his stool . . . rushed over . . . Pop! No patience at all.'

'Now the church by the roundabout that they've started cleaning this week, well I worked there three years ago, in the crypt, damp-proofing, a nice job it was. But I was working with the niece's cousin and that man is a bleeding animal. So he only nicks eight babies' skulls, puts clocks in 'em and flogs 'em down the market. Nicked an old lady's arm as well and hit the guvnor over the head with it. Still got the skin on it and a hundred years old, last person to be buried there and he nicks her arm.'

'Well, if you want to know about hedgehogs then Ronnie's your man. Now he is what I would call an expert. Our garden was full of them when we lived in Acton, and our collie, Queenie, went out after them and you'd hear her going, woo-woo-woo, as she got the prickles stuck in her nose, it took her a year to work out how to get her nose underneath them and flip them over onto their backs, and then she was away, used to rip their bellies out with one bite, but it took her a year.'

15.4.1983   Norwich, 9.30 a.m.

The gales and cold, lashing rain have disappeared overnight and half-timbered Norwich is bathed in glorious sunshine like a picture postcard. I pedal over to the outdoor market and sit in the sun on a bench eating hot bacon rolls with a cup of tea. On an adjoining bench two lovers are having a tiff. He sits stony-faced, his arms crossed, ignoring her tearful reproaches. She stands forlorn, looking at the ground, then walks away. He continues to sit staring grimly, arms folded. A few minutes later she returns with a red rose she has bought from the market which she places on his lap, then puts her arms round his neck and kisses him on his cheek. He allows her to do so. They get up and leave, he with his hands thrust into his jacket pockets, her with her arm through his. She looks up at him. He looks straight ahead, a little smile of smug satisfaction on his otherwise stern face.

15.4.1983

Went to Yarmouth for the evening to the opening of an exhibition by local artists in the library. Downstairs the caretaker sat behind a desk holding the key to the lavatory for the private view crowd upstairs who stood drinking the usual dreadful wine amongst pictures hung on perforated hardboard walls painted a bilious shade of pea green. The pictures had titles such as 'Chromatic Event', 'Nocturne II', 'Loneliness' and 'Sheds near Wissett'. A feeling like the onset of seasickness came over me and I fled to the pub. Never even saw the sea. Drove back through the night across flat, bleak East Anglia, the sky enormous and filled with cold stars. Somewhere out there the missile bases, the lights could be a mile away or ten; this is a landscape which could breed madness.

29.4.1983   Madrid: Metro Nunez de Balboa

At the bottom of the Metro escalator a young Arab beggar girl in a thin cotton dress pressing herself against the moving rubber handrail, rotating her hips and wailing with closed eyes.

9.7.1983   London: St John Street, EC1, midnight

The moon shines over the underground car park. The black and white cat emerges from the darkness of the car park and stops beneath an advertising hoarding of a barebacked blonde in a black leather skirt fastened with thongs. The cat pricks its ears, sniffs the air, and glances to left and right. A newspaper delivery van screams round the corner laden with Sunday colour supplements. The cat waits, then miaows loudly. A black kitten runs out of the car park and halts beside the mother cat. The mother cat runs quickly alongside the car-park fence and stops beneath a poster of a two-toned shoe against the background of the Eiffel Tower. The cat calls and the kitten runs to join it. A motorbike roars past. The cat and the kitten freeze in the shadow of the fence. The cat runs ahead to the corner of the car-park fence, calls, and the kitten scampers after. Three juggernaut lorries filled with dead meat from Armagh rumble down the road in convoy. The cat and the kitten hide and wait. The mother cat moves to the edge of the pavement and looks both ways, calls, the kitten follows, then they run across the road together and into the darkness of the doorway of the knife shop. Two shouting drunks stagger past the doorway, across the road and stand side by side as they piss up against an advertising hoarding of womens' thighs. The cat scuttles out of the doorway and calls the kitten. The cat and the kitten run up the lane and under the perimeter fence of the computer building.

29.8.1983   In the hospital (with my hernia)

A police constable recovering from an operation for ingrown hair in the arsehole and unable to sit down, is standing by his bed dressed only in a nappy covered with a pair of plastic pants, his hands behind his back, rocking backwards and forwards on his heels. In the next bed another ingrown hair sufferer in plastic pants is lying face down; his girlfriend crouched by the bedside is running her tongue around the rim of his ear. A man in a dressing gown, his pyjamas buttoned up to the neck shuffles past carrying a see-through plastic bag into which his urine drips.

A smiling nurse advances towards another man in plastic pants who is lying on his back with his knees raised. She pushes a trolley on which is a large syringe, a container of quick-drying resin, and a canister of laughing gas. She draws the curtains around the bed. From behind the curtains comes the sound of squirting and muffled giggles.

Two smiling men with open wounds, wearing headphones, are watching television. On screen men are being slashed, skewered, disembowelled and shot, their limbs torn off, their brains blown out.

Midnight. The ward is dimly lit by the shaded lamp over the night nurse's desk. In the morning seven men are to be operated on. Two are asleep, five are awake. I am twiddling my thumbs; my left hand is marked with a letter 'L' in felt pen to indicate which side of the body should be operated on. Another man is biting his nails and glancing at his watch. The man in the next bed is staring at the ceiling. He says: 'It's like waiting to be hung, innit?' In the corridor on the other side of the glass doors the man in the wheelchair, his left leg marked for amputation, smokes a last cigarette as he waits for the seven sleeping pills to take effect. Next to him sits a man with a shaven head, on the top of which is a felt pen 'X'.

The frail old deaf-mute in striped pyjamas stands in the

middle of the ward staring blankly ahead, clutching his rosary in his right hand, on the back of which is a letter 'R'.

The long night drags on, punctuated by the steady drip of the urine bags.

In the morning all is hustle and bustle. Washing, shaving, getting ready. Nurses stride purposefully back and forth. The doctors tour the ward, pressing flesh. Patients are wheeled out half-doped and smiling wanly, then wheeled back in unconscious. In the afternoon people come round from the anaesthetic one by one. The first sense to return is hearing. Then sight. The deaf-mute opens his eyes wide, feebly tries to lift both hands, then sinks back into unconsciousness. Behind closed curtains an African youth is sobbing, 'Dadda, Dadda'. The police constable in his plastic pants is patrolling the ward, his hands behind his back. Four men are seated at a table eating steamed fish.

18.10.1983   London, in the pub

The Scholar speaks:

'You know, I got a book out of the library, Finsbury Library, historical. I like anything historical. It was a biography. The whole life, right? Eight hundred and eighty eight pages long. It was the whole life of . . . what's his name? . . . Oh gawd, it's gone right out of my mind . . . what's his name for Christ's sake? Anyway, fantastic it was. What a book! I wish I could remember his name . . . And I got another one out about Sigmund Freud. The whole life of Sigmund Freud the psychiatrist. Now there was a man! What a lot he had to put up with. Did you know he had 22 operations for cancer of the throat? 22! They had to burn out his tonsils with a red hot iron, it was cigars that did it. And eventually he had to have an amputation. Honest. Fair turned my stomach it did, can't stand the sight of blood, when I went to St Barts and they asked me to give a blood sample I said no way . . . The one I've got now is about Anne Boleyn, and did you know that she was executed with a cold blade? Fair enough, neither did I, but it's true, it hurts more that way see. And if you go to Madame Tussauds you'll see that very guillotine. Very small it is, nowhere near as big as you'd think.'

15.11.1983   London: The Highway, E1, 3.15 p.m.

A cold, damp day. On one side of the white line half the road is steaming, the other half is not. A man stands on the pavement by the steaming side staring at the road, pointing his finger and cursing it.

16.11.1983   London: The Kebab House, St John Street, EC1

Two diners sit at a table eating spiced sausages beneath a television with picture but no sound. The man impales a section of sausage and puts it in his mouth, as does the small child on the television screen above his head. The woman cuts a small portion of sausage and lifts it to her lips. On screen pink hands cram meat into a mincer which extrudes curling worms of mince. The woman chews appreciatively, her fork poised in mid-air. The man pours a glass of wine. On screen intestinal membrane is stretched over a nozzle. Minced meat squirts out of the nozzle into the membrane casing and forms a long sausage. The man and the woman eat the last sections of their sausages at the same time, raise their glasses together, dab their lips with their serviettes simultaneously and smile contentedly at each other.

22.12.1983   No. 171 bus to Waterloo

The glassy-eyed girl from the typing pool, drunk after the office party, is singing 'Away In A Manger'. On her lap she clutches her polythene doggie-bag of fruit trifle. '. . . no crib for a bed'. The bus staggers along, stopping and starting in the Christmas shopping traffic. Her face grows paler. '. . . the little Lord Jesus lay down his sweet head'. The bus lurches to a halt in front of a mammoth woman in a fur coat and her small husband following behind laden with parcels. The typist turns white, her gorge rises as she looks around in despair, then vomits into her bag of trifle.

13.1.1984   1.35 train from London to Audley End

Four pinstriped stockbrokers playing cards and kicking each other under the table.

24.2.1984   Metropolitan line tube train from Whitechapel to Farringdon, 3.47 p.m.

Two Chinamen eating bananas.
   1st Chinaman: 'Of all disease, like cancer best.'
   2nd Chinaman: 'Aah-haah! Cancer my favourite also. Cancer number one. Have a banana.'

25.2.1984

A young man and young woman sitting side by side in front of a clock. An hour passes in silence. They react politely when someone sits down nearby or borrows a match, or hangs their coat on the hook behind them, or the barmaid changes the ashtray. After an hour it is closing time. She, pulling on her coat, glances towards him and says brightly: 'OK?' He, pulling on his gloves and gathering up his cigarettes and matches says decisively: 'OK'. They leave.

13.8.1984   London, in the pub

The Patriot speaks:

'Now you take these Olympic Games. You see how well they've done there. And it's not surprising. It's a fact of nature that animals run faster, jump further, swim quicker than human beings. Always have done and always will. And the animals of the jungle are the fleetest of foot. A horse will outrun a man, no matter how hard he tries, but the cheetah will outrun the horse. The panther will outjump any man, the gorilla will lift weights beyone the scope of any human, and the monkey will do gold medal gymnastics all fucking day. It stands to reason. But what I want to know is, why should we have to watch it? Every time you switch on the telly what do you see? A big black woman with rubbery lips gazing up at the Union Jack with tears in her eyes while they're playing 'God Save The Queen'. God help the Queen I say, Christ knows what she must think of it all. And every film you watch they're there. You can't watch a film that's made in the last ten years that isn't full of them. It all started with West Side Story, that was the thin end of the wedge. You see, when Queen Victoria said that all Empire citizens were welcome here she knew very well that they'd have to fucking swim it. Well times change. She didn't anticipate the aeroplane. How was she to know? But now they can come by aeroplane, by train, by boat, they can come by bleeding submarine. Well they should let them come by boat, the biggest boats there are, a whole fleet, and when they're in the middle of the sea we should bomb the fucking lot. Argue about it afterwards I say. They should stop these experiments on animals and use niggers instead.'

21.8.1984   London: St John Street, EC1, 8.10 p.m.

A big hand holding a silver spoon is smashing an egg in an eggcup shaped like a little man's body with outstretched arms. Three identical sweat-soaked men in leather overalls and caps are wielding hammers in unison, their glistening chests and arms lit by the fire of the forge. In front of them, a young man and woman in white tee-shirts, he with a blackened right eye, she with a blackened left eye, are walking along the pavement with their flaxen-haired daughter skipping ahead of them.

23.8.1984   London E1

The dockside warehouse which has been converted into luxury flats stands alongside a scrapyard piled high with metal in a quagmire of black mud. A woman in a fashionwear boiler suit is polishing the windows of the flat on the second floor. In the scrapyard down below three men in wellington boots and swarf-covered overalls stand ankle deep in the mire watching two filthy Alsatian guard dogs fucking in a puddle of oil. The dogs' tongues loll out of the side of their jaws. The dog starts to bark and the bitch begins to howl. The men clap and cheer. A passing pleasure boat sounds its siren. A mother walking by with her little son quickly draws his attention to the nice new flats, pointing up to the second floor where the woman is still slowly polishing the window and running her tongue between her lipsticked teeth.

18.9.1984   Spain, Costa del Sol

The sun blazes down from a cloudless blue sky. On the beach six mangy Andalusian dogs roam amongst the thatched parasols, following a white bitch on heat. Two German honeymooners walk hand in hand out of the tranquil, gin-clear sea, past two youths who sit on the rocks tearing apart live octopuses. The Germans gaze into each other's eyes as they dry each others suntanned bodies, then place their towels beside their beach blanket and walk arm in arm to the taverna. Three little brown babies toddle along the water's edge, gurgling happily. A police helicopter flies overhead. Each of the dogs in turn pisses on the Germans' beach blanket then lopes off after the white bitch alongside the wire fence surrounding the swimming pool around which huge old women lie stretched out in the broiling sun like fish on slabs. The Germans finish their sangria and stroll back down to the shore, her head on his shoulder, then sink down onto the beach blanket in a lingering embrace.

5.10.1984   Matlock Bath, Derbyshire

The cliffs towering above the gorge were floodlit and fairy lights lit up the banks of the River Derwent on which drifted a pageant of illuminated floats in the shapes of peacocks, gondolas and railway engines.

By 1 a.m. the lights were turned off for the night and the admiring crowds had all gone home. A full moon shone over the gorge. All was quiet except for the distant chanting of '*Sieg Heil! Sieg Heil!*' from the wooded valley far below.

21.12.1984   London: St John Street, EC1, 10.50 a.m.

Through an open window comes the sound of voices singing: 'Whence Comes That Goodly Fragrance?' Lying in the middle of the road between the two streams of traffic are two men miming the motions of sexual intercourse. A man in a white coat, peering through the talons of two plucked turkeys which are draped round his neck, steps around the two men as he crosses from one pavement to the other. On the opposite side of the street six pale-faced men are punching each other.

4.4.1985.   London, 5.30 p.m.

The doctor's surgery is held in the local medical mission. A poster immediately inside the door says: 'What think ye of Christ?' No receptionist, just a dimly lit hall with a circle of chairs, on a few of which sit old ladies chewing their lips. On a table in the centre of the hall is a pile of religious pamphlets and magazines about missionaries. Around the walls are more fading posters: 'Come Unto Me and thou shalt be Cleansed', 'Behold I Come Quickly'; 'Jesus Heals the Paralytic'.

5.35 p.m.

Something moves against my leg and a big black cat appears, walks into the centre of the room and sits staring at each sick person in turn. A nun puts her head round the door and then goes away.

5.38 p.m.

I remember a summer night about 25 years ago on the banks of Forbes Pond, a railway ballast hole in Long Eaton, Derbyshire, when after fishing for two nights in succession I dozed off just before dawn. When I woke I looked to my right and out of the mist drifting over the pond a black dog emerged from below the water, crawled to the edge and climbed the shale embankment to the railway line. The ripples settled. The grebes began to dive. Fish broke surface without a sound. The flannel-weed moved and a large V-wave spread across the pond. I heard a twig snap and turned round. A nun stood in the bushes, watching me. She turned and walked away into the mist.

5.40 p.m.

The only other time I fell asleep at that pond was two summers later. I arrived just after dusk at my favourite spot beneath the railway embankment, then found that I had forgotten my portable deckchair which I usually had strapped to the crossbar of my bicycle. I spread my waterproof cycle cape on the ground and sat on it. The fish were not feeding, I'd had a few pints on my way to the pond, and I lay back on the cape. I fell asleep. I woke some time later with the sensation of something sitting on my chest. I opened my eyes: it was a big rat. I jumped to my feet but the rat clung on to my clothing until I hit it and it lost its hold and scurried off into the reeds together with the many other rats which had gathered around me.

5.43 p.m.

Another night my mate who I was fishing with fell asleep with his head resting on a loaf of bread as a pillow; by the morning the rats had tunnelled through the loaf, leaving just the crust beneath his head like a pillow case.

5.45 p.m.

Years later I was living in a basement flat in South London.
The people next door threw all their garbage out of the back
window. Inevitably there were rats. My cat would catch them
and bring them into the flat alive and let them run around
while it sat watching them. One night I came back from the
pub and the cat was sitting in the middle of the room, purring
and thumping its tail on the floor. There was a rat inside one
of my shoes and another one behind the record-player. I
carried the shoe outside, tipped out the rat and stuck a knife
through its head. The rat squealed and blood spurted onto
my hands. I couldn't bear to kill the other one so I trapped it
in a cardboard tube and carried it down the street before
letting it go. It ran off across the zebra crossing.

5.50 p.m.

In March last year I arrived home at midnight, exhausted
after a long train journey. A note had been pushed under the
door of my third floor flat. It was from the meat firm on the
first floor, and said:

'Dear Ian,
Just to let you know that there are rats downstairs in our
offices. Apparently they have come up from the Chinese
bean sprout factory in the basement. We have called in
Rentokil but the poisons they are leaving are not
proving very effective. The reason we are warning you is
that they are burrowing up the walls.'

Needless to say it was a sleepless night as I lay awake
listening to every sound.
Tick Tock. 5.57 pm by the clock on the wall, 5.59 pm by my
watch.

I remember a day 11 years ago. I was standing at a bus stop, waiting for a bus, of which there was no sign. I glanced at my wristwatch and thought: 'I'm going to be late.' I wondered where the bus was and imagined a traffic jam south of the Elephant & Castle, in the middle of which was the red bus. I thought: 'Will I get to the library before closing time?' and in my mind's eye I could see the library assistants glancing at the clock on the wall, waiting to press the 15 minutes to closing time bell. The traffic crawled across the bridge, one person in each car, encapsulated, tight-lipped, hands clutching the steering wheels, knuckles white. A boat hooted on the river. Behind me was a cinema; what was on the screen: a jungle scene, a murder, a passionate embrace? On the other side of the road was a theatre; what was on the stage: a domestic drawing room, a battle, a grief-stricken man on his knees? I could hear snatches of the conversation of the other people in the bus queue: 'So, I said to him, don't touch it . . . it's always the same . . . the very idea . . . all over the floor.' I remembered another bus queue, 35 years ago on the opposite side of Canal Street, Long Eaton, as the small boy (me) wearing his Road Safety Poster Competition winner's medal, ran out from behind the parked lorry straight into the path of the oncoming cyclist, and the women in the bus queue screamed in unison. As I looked at my wristwatch I could see my own face reflected in the watch glass and also the tower block behind me with its hundreds of windows, behind which . . .? It was six o'clock. No sign of the bus. 'I'm going to be late.'

6.05 p.m.

'Next patient please.'

28.6.1985   London: St John Street, EC1

A man is staring at a puddle. He inspects it from three different positions. Then he walks away, sighs, shrugs his shoulders and says: 'With puddles like that there's no hope for us.'

12.10.1985   London

Voices in a bar bring back memories of other voices in other bars. One voice leads to another until the voices and the memories intertwine.

'Winner breaks.' 'Lovely boy! Never be another one like him!' 'Ah cud dow weea pint, gerrumin yoth!' 'It's a spot, you're on stripes.' 'All right, switch the light on, put the mat down, throw for partners, nearest and furthest.' 'Oi, oi, let the dog see the rabbit!' 'Fair enough, it's George and Pat and Terry and Beryl.' 'Two shots.' 'Call them chickens? I tell you the chickens round here are so bleeding small they'd pass for bleeding sparrows. In fact I thought of taking one back home for my budgie, he's very amorous, I thought I'll take it back, stick it on his perch and say there you are old son get stuck into that, all done up in a polythene bag and everything, he'd revel in it once it thawed out.' 'Heads or tails? Tails, you to chalk.' 'Carry the shot.' '301, you to start.' 'Eyup mi owd! Aahs it gooin?' 'A'm ayin wun fer t'body tedee, sorrey. Ah wer gooin tuh goo tuh wok laik, burrah overlaid. En that there snipey-nosed pisspot ah've got furra foreman, eh'd ave ony gone tellin tales t'boss if ah'd ave tonned up lait, so ah thot tuh missen bogger it ah'll stay at om.' 'Arrers Tel, arrers!' 'Lovely boy! Never be another one like him!' 'Light and bitter, is it?' 'In a straight glass.' 'All of the news of all of the world, what does it all add up to eh? Nothing. Yesterday's newspapers today's chipwrappers. All of the books ever written: no more than a fart in the wind. All the songs ever sung: wasted breath. All the pictures ever painted: they might just as well have painted their toenails. All the jokes ever told: just laughing to keep from crying. All the wars that were ever fought, what did they achieve? Bugger all. They just put people out of their misery a bit quicker that's all. The tyrants die, the heroes die, the villains die, the heroines die, every one the same. All the accidents: all the car smashes and the plane crashes, the drownings, the burnings, the suffocations, the floods, famines, earthquakes, tornadoes and eruptions of volcanoes, they were all going to die anyway sooner or later. Aren't we all? Yes, same again please, pint of mixed.' 'Free ball.' 'You've got to have eyes in your arse.' 'Who's on dukes?' 'Twenty Bensons please, Julie.' 'This beer's like weazel waz.' 'Of course she'd had diarrhoea for a year you know.' 'That's my man. And again. Double top you want Beryl. Unlucky!' 'And those Mexicans prancing around in their sombreros, they're not doing anything that hasn't been done on television.' 'Lovely boy! Never be another one like him!' 'Cover the orange.' 'Did you know that my brother's feet are completely septic?' 'No, actually I didn't.' 'Well, he runs five miles every morning before breakfast with a concrete block in each hand, so I said to him well what can you expect?' 'Quite.' 'It serves him right, don't you think?' 'Absolutely.' 'Two garden gates.' 'Bring in the dogs I say.' 'OK?' 'All right, an aeroplane falls out of the sky. Two hundred passengers killed. Was it a bomb they say, or instrument failure, did someone leave a door open? Maybe all four engines dropped off? Who knows? Old Charlie Fort could have thought up a hundred different reasons just as likely. But what if half way across the ocean Captain Smith just thought, "Ah, fuck it, let's go." Flips a switch. Still smiling as the plane hits the waves. No, no, it's my round, you bought the last one. No, I insist. Oh, all right then, I'll have a drop of Teacher's, no ice. I'll get the next one in.' 'Feathers.

Any way you like.' 'Two pound forty to you squire.' 'Double it in the middle.' 'An Abbot by the neck and a Bishop's Finger please.' 'Take it off the top cushion.' 'Toilet's blocked, television's on the blink, the phone's gone dead, it's been one of those days.' 'Two beehives.' 'Their bodies all charred, bones sticking out, flesh dropping off in lumps, like a school dinner.' 'Lovely boy! Never be another one like him.' 'Not a bad pint tonight.' 'Fuckin' chateau sorrey!' 'Two weeks in Egypt this year, the weather was extraordinary, but the pyramids, my God, you wouldn't believe it, they've got squatters! It's true! The base of the pyramids is a honeycomb of caves and tunnels and they're filled with the riffraff of Cairo.' 'Two Tom Mixes.' 'Half an ounce of Golden Virginia.' 'Ha, ha!' 'D'yo fancy a game uh crib our kid? Wey cud gerron th'end uh that table there if them two utched up a bit?' 'Ah's not essa bothered Brian. Burrahl ay an and uh brag wi yer till Rita turns up f'yo like?' 'Raight, yer on.' 'See that woman in the paper, got the flu 27 years ago and stayed in bed ever since until the day she died? Just wouldn't get out of bed. They said she wasted her life, but who are they to say? What did she have to get up for? She'd only have had to rush about doing things like the rest of us. At least she was warm all the year round.' 'But if I was black or if I had cancer.' 'Do you want the two?' 'Yellow in the corner pocket.' 'A sausage made of pure veal.' 'A dartboard on the patio.' 'Lovely boy! Never be another one like him!' 'Now would I lie to you babe? On my life.' 'Gin and Tonic, Bacardi and Coke, Campari and Soda, two glasses of white wine and five packets of Smokey Bacon crisps.' 'Ha! Ha! Ha!' 'Agreed, agreed, but let me just sketch out a little scenario for you, OK? Let's imagine your typical early morning train, there's a whole carriage full of people all worried about something or other. The old man in the corner is worried about his pension. The woman opposite him is worried because the train's late and she might miss her connection. The man across the aisle on his way to a business

116

conference, he's frowning and chain-smoking, he's trying to write his speech. Grandma's worried about her son Tony and his wife and the new baby, Margaret's ever so tired and weepy since the birth and little Tracey's sickening for sure. Are you with me so far? Right. Now Margaret, she sits opposite, washed out, worried, and she's got Tracey grizzling on her knee. OK? While Tony, sitting alongside her, he's worrying about Margaret and Tracey and his mother, she's not as young as she was; if only he could get a job, earn some decent money and get them a house and a bungalow nearby for mum maybe. And the man in the window seat he's just moved into a new flat and discovered that the previous tenant was homosexual and now he's worried sick that he might have caught AIDS by cleaning out the toilet with a cut on his hand, that's right, incubating inside him right now maybe, it'll be months or even years before he knows for sure and then it'll be too late, there's a lot of worry ahead. Meanwhile, ten miles up the bleedin' track a bunch of spotty-faced kids are busy hanging an iron girder on a rope from the railway bridge, while one of them keeps a lookout in the road, hopping from foot to foot, a bag of nerves, worried they'll get caught see? Just a half for me thanks. And three minutes later the train hits the girder, wallop! Takes the top of the cab off and the driver's head with it. All the carriages get derailed and mashed up like concertinas, bodies everywhere, absolute mayhem. Here, have one of mine. And all of them worrying right up to the last minute. Fat lot of good it did them, eh? Dear oh dear they never knew what hit them. Grandma killed, Margaret killed, Tracey killed outright. Tony lives on for another 30 years in a wheelchair, the businessman gets blinded, and the bloke who thinks he's got AIDS gets saved with a blood transfusion so he's still fuckin' worried! Cheers. And the kids who did the clever little trick with the girder, they all scarper; one dies the next month on his motorbike, two get nicked and rot away in clink, and the fourth one gets clean away, joins the merchant navy and sails the seas for years, then he retires and buys a little bungalow by the seaside and potters about the garden for a few months then drops down dead with a heart attack one day while he's planting his lettuce, so he just went later that's all. You get my meaning? Oh my God, look who just walked in, here comes trouble! Ronnie, you scoundrel, where've you been hiding out, it must be over a year, what do you want to drink you old tow-rag?' 'Lovely boy! Never be another one like him.' 'Who wants eels? Ray? Karen? Steve? Tina?' 'Two pints of Pedigree and a Snowball.' 'She looked like she'd spent the last six weeks sitting on a cold custard.' 'There's a plant on.' 'It's raight back-end weather int it?' 'Ay burrit cud be woss. They reckon uz ow it's silin dahn in Derby.' 'Gerraht?!' ' 'Sraight. En yo look aht t'dooer, it's gerrin a bit black ovver Borrowash. Ah wunna be surprised if it inna reenin ere an all bi chuckin aht time.' 'Lovely boy! Never be another one like him!' 'Can you see it?' 'No.' 'Come back up the table then.' 'Two pints of Ordinary and a Ramrod.' 'They went to Majorca, right? And they met these Swedish birds, right? And the things they didn't do aint worth a mention. It's all on Polaroid, I'm going to see then Thursday.' 'Hot soup, colour TV. Soon be Christmas. It's all down to the microwave chip innit?' 'And a box of Swan.' 'Deep screw into the centre. Watch the in-off though.' 'See that couple sitting side by side over in the corner, her with her handbag on her knees and him tapping his fingers on the table, they've been married for 30 years. Never say a word to each other all night, not even when he gets the drinks in. They might just as well put their heads in the oven. Do themselves a favour. They could do it together, save on the gas bill and needn't say a word even then.' 'So what broke up the team? Buggery, that's what did it.' 'Anyone for an eyeball?' 'There's been a really interesting series of documentaries on the radio, have you been listening to them?' 'No, what were they about?' 'I can't remember.'

'All the sixteens.' 'Put us a half in there Chris.' 'Lovely boy! Never be another one like him!' 'Take my shot while I get a pint.' 'My first wife was one of the George Mitchell Singers.' 'Enough said.' 'This guide dog needs some proper training Ronnie, he'd shag a bleeding chair leg. Get down you randy sod!' 'Ev yo dun owt much todee?' 'Norra lot. Ah went dahn tahn s'afto burrit wer snyded aht wi folk, so ah took our Shane along t'cut 'n back, ed mi tee, an ah wer gunna do a bit in t'gardin burrit looked laik it wer tonnin te reen, so ah cum arairnd furra jar. Worrabout yo?' 'Too much left-hand side.' 'Two large Bells please.' 'Lovely boy! Never be another one like him.' 'Follow through onto the green if you can. If not then leave the white safe on the top cush.' 'I read this book, about France in the eighteenth century, and in it was this philosopher, a very educated man, never had to get his hands dirty. Well one morning just like any other he goes through his usual routine: has a lie-in, breakfast in bed about 11 o'clock, washes, shaves, powders his wig, chooses his clothes for the day and gets dressed, ties his cravat just right then sets off to stroll down to the coffee shop to spend the afternoon philosophizing with his mates, and as he goes out the door of his house he stubs his toe on the step, says "Sod it" or whatever the French for that is, takes out his pistol and blows his brains out. Say what you like, they had style in those days. Better than that stupid git in Poland who hammered four six-inch nails into his head then changed his mind, staggered to the hospital and dropped dead on the step. No style at all the Poles.' 'Ha! Ha! Ha! Ha!' 'Right, let's be having you! We've got to go to bed even if you haven't!' 'Tucked it in the corner! Very nice!' 'Shift that black.' 'Last game on the dartboard!' 'Shot!' 'And the the pool!' 'Shot!' 'There are more obscene telephone calls in the Hebrides per head of population than anywhere else in Western Europe, and in Orkney the poison pen letters defy belief.' 'Well I never!' 'Eyup yoth, ev yo erd this'n? Oh man und iz missis guz tuh

Marriage Guidance Clinic, raight? 'N oh man sez, "Ah reckon uz ow she's frigid laik, or else ahm dooin summat wrong, cos when weer, y'know, when wey mek love laik, she never sighs nuh moans or owt." So t'doctor sez to er, "Do yo love yerusband?" 'N she sez, "Ah do unnall, e's grand uz owt." So t'doctor sez, "Well then, yo mon't be afraid tuh sho it." So t'next time they's on t'nest laik, 'n oh's just abaht on t'vinegar stroke, she sez, "Tell me when tuh moan," and e sez, "Moan nah! Moan nah!" un she guz, "Yuh never elp wi t'washin up! Yuh never elp wi t'washin up!" ' 'Heh! Heh! Heh! That's a raight good un sorrey! Bogger me, that's a brahma!' 'Well, worrabaht the wun abaht er from t'manor und the white oss?' 'Ah've erd it.' 'The trouble with your friend is he's knitted to death.' 'Lovely boy, never be another one like him.' 'Where's the chalk?' 'Oh do drop in!' 'Come on you's two lovebirds, time to go to bubbyoes!' 'My breasts are like a battlefield.' 'Ha! Ha! Ha!' 'All the vegetables and the vitamins and the honeycombs you can chuck them out the window and chuck yourself out after. Honey won't save you. Money won't save you. Bugs Bunny won't save you any more than Mother Teresa, Karl Marx or Jesus Fucking Christ! All the vegetarians will die and so will the cows and the pigs and the chickens. All the doctors will die as well as all the patients. The people who make the bombs will die and the people who camp outside the bomb bases will die whether the bombs go off or not. Now am I right or am I wrong?' 'Ha! Ha! Ha!' 'You go off, play pool, leave me here, I had to buy a double vodka for myself!' 'Well if you want to be a piss-artist that's up to you innit?' 'Berrer tuh walk up 'n dahn 'n do nowt than set ut om 'n rot.' 'OK? Twat?!' 'Haven't you got no homes to go to?!' 'Ha! Ha! Ha! Ha! Dear oh dear!' 'Can we have your glasses please?! It's well after time!' 'Ha! Ha! Ha!' 'Cab? Yes, in the lounge, him by the window. Finish your drinks please, the Law's outside!' 'His hand in my glove.' 'Ha! Ha! Ha! Ha! Go on! Ha! Ha! Ha!' 'Now are you going to drink that, or am I going to have to take it away from you?' 'All right, all right, keep your hair on.' 'Well drink up then, this is the last time of asking.' 'I am drinking up.' 'No you're not. Now finish that drink.' 'OK. OK. I heard you the first time.' 'Never mind the lip, finish that drink.' 'Fuckinada sunshine, what do you do for fun?' 'Right! Onyer bike! Out!' 'Ha! Ha! Ha! Ha! Well ah'll guh te Trent! Ha! Ha! Bogger me!' 'Lovely boy! Never be another one like him!' 'Come on Arthur! Come on Steve! And you Rita!' 'Ha! Ha! Ha! Ha! Yuh never elp wi t'washin up! Ha! Ha! Ha! Ha! Ha! Ha!' 'Savings banks, blood banks, sperm banks, you might just as well piss in the sea. All the babies born today will die. Every single one. See you Ronnie, mind how you go. All their plans and schemes and hopes and dreams they'll come to the same end as yours and mine: blackout, game over. It's a downhill struggle from the day that you're born. The most you can hope for is to die in your sleep. You and me both. Cheers Micky, take care, yes see you Sunday all being well.' 'Ha! Ha! Ha! Ha!' 'Come on you's lot, onyer bikes!' 'Cheers Arthur!' 'Cheers Steve!' 'Bye Paula!' 'See you Ray!' 'Ha! Ha! Ha! Ha! Ha!' 'All the best Sheila!' 'So long Patsy!' 'Goodnight Ian!' 'Goodnight all!' 'Ha! Ha! Ha! You have to laugh!'